The World's Wit and Humor

The World's Wit and Humor

An Encyclopedia of the Classic Wit and Humor of all Ages and Nations

American, British, French, German, Italian, Spanish, Russian, Scandinavian, Greek, Roman, Oriental and Miscellaneous

Fifteen Volumes, with Portrait Frontispieces and Many Cartoons

International Board of Editors

Joel Chandler Harris
American

Andrew Lang
British

Brander Matthews
Continental European

William Hayes Ward
Greek, Roman and Oriental

Horatio Sheafe Krans, *Associate American*

Lionel Strachey, *Managing Editor*

New York
The Review of Reviews Company
1906

Miguel de cerbantes

The World's Wit and Humor

ITALIAN—SPANISH

Volume XIII

Boccaccio to d'Amicis

———

Mendoza to Valdés

New York

The Review of Reviews Company

1906

THE QUINN & BODEN PRESS
RAHWAY, N. J.

Table of Contents

vii

Italian Wit and Humor

Table of Contents

Spanish Wit and Humor

Table of Contents

Spanish Wit and Humor

Acknowledgments

We beg to tender courteous acknowledgment to the following publishers for the use of extracts appearing in this volume:

CASSELL & COMPANY: The Account-Book, by PEDRO DE ALARCON, in "Moors and Christians."

BRENTANO'S: Founding a Provincial Newspaper, from PALACIO VALDÉS' "The Fourth Estate."

Italian and Spanish
Wit and Humor

Italian Wit and Humor

Giovanni Boccaccio

The One-Legged Crane

MASTER CURRADO GIANFILIAZZI, as most of you have seen and know, living in the estate of a noble citizen, being a man bountiful, magnificent, and within the degree of knighthood, continually kept both hawks and hounds, taking no mean delight in such pleasures as they yielded, neglecting for them far more serious employments, wherewith our present subject presumeth not to meddle. Upon a day, having killed with his falcon a crane, near to a village called Peretola, and finding her to be young and fat, he sent it to his cook, a Venetian born, named Chichibio, with command to have it prepared for his supper. Chichibio, who resembled no other than (as he was indeed) a plain, simple, honest, merry fellow, having dressed the crane as it ought to be, put it on the spit and laid it to the fire.

When it was well near roasted, and gave forth a very delicate pleasing savor, it happened that a young woman dwelling not far off, named Brunetta, and of whom Chichibio was somewhat enamored, entered into the kitchen, and feeling the excellent smell of the crane to please her beyond all savors that ever she had felt before, she entreated Chichibio very earnestly that he would bestow a leg thereof upon her. Whereto Chichibio, like a pleasant companion, and evermore delighting in singing, sung her this answer:

"My Brunetta, fair and feat, no, no.
Why should you say so? Oh, oh!

The meat of my master
Takes you for no taster.
Go from the kitchen—go!"

Many other speeches passed between them in a short
while, but, in the end, Chichibio, because he would not have
his mistress Brunetta angry with him, cut off one of the
crane's legs from the spit and gave it to her to eat.

Afterward, when the fowl was served up to the table
before Currado, who had invited certain strangers his friends
to sup with him, wondering not a little, he called for Chichibio his cook, demanding what was become of the crane's
other leg. Whereto the Venetian, being a liar by nature,
suddenly answered, "Sir, cranes have no more but one leg
each bird." Currado, growing very angry, replied, "Wilt
thou tell me that a crane hath no more than one leg? Did
I never see a crane before this?" Chichibio, persisting reso-
lutely in his denial, said, "Believe me, sir, I have told you
nothing but the truth; and when you please I will make good
my words by such fowls as are living."

Currado, in kind love to the strangers that he had invited
to supper, gave over any further contestation; only he said,
"Seeing thou assurest me to let me see thy affirmation for
truth by other of the same fowls living—a thing which as
yet I never saw or heard of—I am content to make proof
thereof to-morrow morning. Till then I shall rest satisfied.
But, upon my word, if I find it otherwise, expect such a
sound payment as thy knavery justly deserveth, to make
thee remember it all thy lifetime."

The contention ceasing for the night, Currado, who, although he had slept well, remained still discontented in his
mind, arose in the morning by break of day, and puffing and

blowing angrily, called for his horses, commanding Chichibio to mount on one of them; so riding on toward the river, where early every morning he had seen plenty of cranes, he said to his man, "We shall see anon, sirrah, whether thou or I lied yesternight."

Chichibio, perceiving that his master's anger was not as yet assuaged, and that now it stood him upon to make good his lie, not knowing how he should do it, rode after his master fearfully trembling all the way. Gladly he would have made an escape, but he could not by any possible means, and on every side he looked about him, now before and after behind, to espy any cranes standing on both their legs, which would have been an ominous sight to him. But being come near to the river he chanced to see, before any of the rest, upon the bank thereof about a dozen cranes in number, each standing upon one leg, as they use to do when they are sleeping. Whereupon, showing them quickly to Currado, he said: "Now, sir, yourself may see whether I told you true yesternight or no. I am sure a crane hath but one thigh and one leg, as all here present are apparent witnesses, and I have been as good as my promise."

Currado, looking at the cranes, and well understanding the knavery of his man, replied, "Stay but a little while, sirrah, and I will show thee that a crane hath two thighs and two legs." Then, riding somewhat nearer to them, he cried out aloud, "Shough! shough!" which caused them to set down their other legs; and all fled away, after they had made a few paces against the wind for their mounting. So, going unto Chichibio, he said, "How now, you lying knave! hath a crane two legs or no?" Chichibio, being well near at his wits' end, not knowing now what answer he should make, but even as it came suddenly in his mind, said, "Sir, I perceive you are in the right; and if you would have done as much yesternight, and have cried 'Shough!' as here you did, questionless, the crane would then have set down the other leg, as these here did. But if, as they, she had fled away, too, by that means you might have lost your supper."

This sudden and unexpected answer, coming from such a logger-headed lout, and so seasonably for his own safety, was so pleasing to Currado, that he fell into a hearty laughter, and, forgetting all anger, said, "Chichibio, thou hast quitted thyself well and to my contentment, albeit I advise thee to try no more such tricks hereafter." Thus Chichibio, by his sudden and merry answer, escaped a sound beating, which otherwise his master had inflicted upon him.

—*"The Decameron."*

Three Girls and Their Talk

By a clear well, within a little field
  Full of green grass and flowers of every hue,
  Sat three young girls, relating (as I knew)
Their loves. And each had twined a bough to shield
Her lovely face; and the green leaves did yield
  The golden hair their shadow; while the two
  Sweet colors mingled, both blown lightly through
With a soft wind forever stirred and stilled.
After a while one of them said,
  "Think you, if, ere the next hour struck,
  Each of our lovers should come here to-day,
Think you that we should fly, or feel afraid?"
  To whom the others answered, "From such luck
  A girl would be a fool to run away."—*The Sonnets.*

6

Giovanni Boccaccio

The Stolen Pig

CALANDRINO had a little farm, not far from Florence, which came to him through his wife. There he used to have a pig fatted every year, and some time about December he and his wife went always to kill and salt it for the use of the family. Now it happened once—she being unwell at the time—that he went thither by himself to kill this pig; which Bruno and Buffalmacco hearing, and knowing she was not to be there, they went to spend a few days with a great friend of theirs, a priest in Calandrino's neighborhood. Now the pig had been killed the very day they came thither, and Calandrino, seeing them along with the priest, called to them and said, "Welcome, kindly; I would gladly you should see what a good manager I am." Then, taking them into the house, he showed them this pig. They saw that it was fat, and were told by him that it was to be salted for his family. "Salted, booby?" said Bruno. "Sell it, let us make merry with the money, and tell your wife that it was stolen." "No," said Calandrino, "she will never believe it; and, besides, she would turn me out of doors. Trouble me, then, no further about any such thing, for I will never do it." They said a great deal more to him, but all to no purpose. At length he invited them to supper, but did it in such a manner that they refused.

After they had come away from him, said Bruno to Buffalmacco, "Suppose we steal this pig from him to-night." "How is it possible?" "Oh, I know well enough how to do it, if he does not remove it in the meantime from the place where we just now saw it." "Then let us do it, and afterward we and the parson will make merry over it." The priest assured them that he should like it above all things. "We must use a little art," quoth Bruno; "you know how covetous he is, and how freely he drinks when it is at another's cost. Let us get him to the tavern, where the parson shall make a pretense of treating us all, out of compliment to him. He will soon get drunk, and then the thing will be easy enough, as there is nobody in the house but himself."

This was done, and Calandrino, finding that the parson was to pay, took his glasses pretty freely, and, getting his dose, walked home betimes, left the door open, thinking that it was shut, and so went to bed. Buffalmacco and Bruno went from the tavern to sup with the priest, and as soon as supper was over they took proper tools with them to get into the house; but finding the door open, they carried off the pig to the priest's and went to bed likewise.

In the morning, as soon as Calandrino had slept off his wine, he rose, came down-stairs, and finding the door open and his pig gone, began to inquire of everybody if they knew anything of the matter; and receiving no tidings of it, he made a terrible outcry, saying, "What shall I do now? Somebody has stolen my pig!" Bruno and Buffalmacco were no sooner out of bed than they went to his house to hear what he would say; and the moment he saw them he roared out, "Oh, my friends, my pig is stolen!" Upon this Bruno whispered to him and said, "Well, I am glad to see you wise in your life for once." "Alas!" quoth he, "it is too true." "Keep to the same story," said Bruno, "and make noise enough for every one to believe you."

Calandrino now began to bawl louder, "Indeed! I vow and swear to you that it is stolen." "That's right; be sure you let everybody hear you, that it may appear so." " Do you think that I would forswear myself about it? May I be hanged this moment if it is not so!" "How is it possible?" quoth Bruno; "I saw it but last night; never imagine that I can believe it." "It is so, however," answered he, "and I am undone. I dare not now go home again, for my wife will never believe me, and I shall have no peace this twelve-month." "It is a most unfortunate thing," said Bruno, "if it be true; but you know I put it into your head to say so last night, and you should not make sport both of your wife and us at the same time."

At this Calandrino began to roar out afresh, saying, "Good God! you make me mad to hear you talk. I tell you once for all it was stolen this very night!" "Nay, if it be so," quoth Buffalmacco, "we must think of some way to get it back again." "And what way must we take," said he, "to find it?" "Depend upon it," replied the other, "that nobody came from the Indies to steal it; it must be somewhere in your neighborhood, and if you could get the people together I could make a charm, with some bread and cheese, that would soon discover the thief." "True," said Bruno, "but they would know in that case what you were about; and the person that has it would never come near you." "How must we manage, then?" said Buffalmacco. "Oh!" replied Bruno, "you shall see me do it with some pills of ginger and a little wine, which I will ask them to come and drink. They will have no suspicion what our design is, and we can make a charm of these as well as of the bread and cheese." "Very well," quoth the other. "What do you say, Calandrino? Have you a mind we should try it?" "For Heaven's sake do," he said; "if I only knew who the thief is, I should be half comforted." "Well, then," quoth Bruno, "I am ready to go to Florence for the things, if you will only give me some money." He happened to have a few florins in his pocket, which he gave him, and off went Bruno.

When he got to Florence, Bruno went to a friend's house and bought a pound of ginger made into pills. He also got two pills made of aloes, which had a private mark that he should not mistake them, being candied over with sugar like the rest. Then, having bought a jar of good wine, he returned to Calandrino, and said, " To-morrow you must take care to invite every one that you have the least suspicion of; it is a holiday, and they will be glad to come. We will finish the charm to-night, and bring the things to your house in the morning, and then I will take care to do and say on your behalf what is necessary upon such an occasion."

Calandrino did as he was told, and in the morning he had nearly all the people in the parish assembled under an elm-tree in the churchyard. His two friends produced the pills and wine, and, making the people stand round in a circle, Bruno said to them, " Gentlemen, it is fit that I should tell you the reason of your being summoned here in this manner, to the end, if anything should happen which you do not like, that I be not blamed for it. You must know, then, that Calandrino had a pig stolen last night, and, as some of the company here must have taken it, he, that he may find out the thief, would have every man take and eat one of these pills, and drink a glass of wine after it. Whoever the guilty person is, you will find he will not be able to get a bit of it down, but it will taste so bitter that he will be forced to spit it out. Therefore, to prevent such open shame, he had better, whoever he is, make a secret confession to the priest, and I will proceed no further."

All present declared their readiness to eat; so, placing

them all in order, he gave every man his pill, and coming to Calandrino, he gave one of the aloe pills to him, which he straightway put into his mouth, and no sooner did he begin to chew it than he was forced to spit it out. Every one was now attentive to see who spit his pill out, and while Bruno kept going round, apparently taking no notice of Calandrino, he heard somebody say behind him, " Hey-day! what is the meaning of its disagreeing so with Calandrino?" Bruno now turned suddenly about, and seeing that Calandrino had spit out his pill, he said, " Stay a little, honest friends, and be not too hasty in judging; it may be something else that has made him spit, and therefore he shall try another." So he gave him the other aloe pill, and then went on to the rest that were unserved. But if the first was bitter to him, this he thought much more so. However, he endeavored to get it down as well as he could. But it was impossible; it made the tears run down his cheeks, and he was forced to spit it out at last, as he had done the other. In the meantime Buffalmacco was going about with the wine; but when he and all of them saw what Calandrino had done, they began to bawl out that he had robbed himself, and some of them abused him roundly.

After they were all gone, Buffalmacco said, " I always thought that you yourself were the thief, and that you were willing to make us believe the pig was stolen in order to keep your money in your pocket, lest we should expect a treat upon the occasion." Calandrino, who had still the taste of the aloes in his mouth, fell a-swearing that he knew nothing of the matter. " Honor bright, now, comrade," said Buffalmacco, " what did you get for it?" This made Calandrino quite furious.

To crown all, Bruno struck in: " I was just now told,"

said he, "by one of the company, that you have a mistress in this neighborhood to whom you are very kind, and that he is confident you have given it to her. You know you once took us to the plains of Mugnone, to look for some black stones, when you left us in the lurch, and pretended you had found them; and now you think to make us believe that your pig is stolen, when you have either given it away or sold it. You have played so many tricks upon us, that we intend to be fooled no more by you. Therefore, as we have had a deal of trouble in the affair, you shall make us amends by giving us two couple of fowls, unless you mean that we should tell your wife."

Calandrino, now perceiving that he would not be believed, and being unwilling to have them add to his troubles by bringing his wife upon his back, was forced to give them the fowls, which they joyfully carried off along with the pork.

—"The Decameron."

Rustico di Filippo

The Making of Master Messerin

WHEN God had finished Master Messerin,
  He really thought it something to have done:
  Bird, man, and beast had got a chance in one,
And each felt flattered, it was hoped, therein.
For he is like a goose i' the windpipe thin,
  And like a camelopard high i' the loins,
  To which for manhood, you'll be told, he joins
Some kind of flesh hues and a callow chin.
As to his singing, he affects the crow,
As to his learning, beasts in general,
  And sets all square by dressing like a man.
God made him, having nothing else to do,
And proved there is not anything at all
  He cannot make, if that's a thing He can.

Cecco Angolieri

What I Should Like to Do

IF I were fire, I'd burn the world away;
　If I were wind, I'd turn my storms thereon;
　If I were water, I'd soon let it drown;
If I were God, I'd sink it from the day;
If I were Pope, I'd never feel quite gay
　Until there was no peace beneath the sun;
　If I were Emperor, what would I have done?
I'd lop men's heads all round in my own way.
If I were death, I'd look my father up;
If I were life, I'd run away from him,
　And treat my mother to like calls and runs.
If I were Cecco—and that's all my hope—
I'd pick the nicest girls to suit my whim,
　And other folk should get the ugly ones.

Luigi Pulci

The Ridiculous End of Morgante and Margutte

MORGANTE took his master's advice and went straight-forward with him through many great adventures, helping him with loving good-will as often as he was permitted, sometimes as his pioneer, and sometimes as the finisher of troublesome work, such as the killing of a few thousand infidels. Now he hurled a spy into a river, now felled a rude ambassador to the earth (for he did not stand upon cere-mony), now cleared a space round him in battle with the clapper of an old bell he had found at the monastery, now doubled up a king in his tent and bore him away, tent and all, and a paladin with him, because he would not let the paladin go.

In the course of these services the giant was left to take care of a lady, and lost his master for a time; and the office being at an end, he set out to rejoin him, when, arriving at a cross-road, he met with a very extraordinary personage. This was a giant huger than himself, swarthy-faced, hor-rible, brutish. He came out of a wood, and appeared to be journeying somewhere. Morgante, who had the great bell-clapper above mentioned in his hand, struck it on the ground with astonishment, as much as to say, "Who the devil is this?" And then he set himself on a stone by the wayside to observe the creature.

"What is your name, traveler?" said Morgante, as it came up.

"My name is Margutte," said the phenomenon. "I intended to be a giant myself, but altered my mind, you see, and stopped half-way, so that I am only twenty feet or so."

"I am glad to see you," quoth his brother giant. "But tell me, are you Christian or Saracen? Do you believe in Christ or in Apollo?"

"To tell you the truth," said the other, "I believe neither in black nor blue, but in a good capon, whether it be roast or boiled. I believe sometimes also in butter, and, when I can get it, in new wine, particularly the rough sort; but, above all, I believe in wine that's good and old. Mahomet's prohibition of it is all moonshine. I am the son, you must know, of a Greek nun and a Turkish bishop, and the first thing I learned was to play the fiddle. I used to sing Homer to it. I was then concerned in a brawl in a mosque, in which the old bishop happened to be killed; so I girded my sword to my side and went to seek my fortune, equipped with all the possible sins of Turkey and Greece. People talk of the seven deadly sins; but I have twenty-seven that never leave me, summer or winter, by which you may judge of the amount of my venial ones. I am a gambler, a cheat, a ruffian, a highwayman, a pickpocket, a glutton (at beef or blows); have no shame whatever; love to let everybody know what I can do; lie about what I cannot do; have a particular attachment to sacrilege; swallow perjury like figs; never give a farthing to anybody; beg of everybody, and abuse them into the bargain; look upon not spilling a drop of liquor as the chief of all cardinal virtues, but must own that I am not much given to assassination, murder being inconvenient; and one thing I am bound to acknowledge, which is, that I never betrayed a comrade."

"That is as well," observed Morgante; "because, you see,

as you don't believe in anything else, I'd have you believe in this bell-clapper of mine. So now, as you have been candid with me, and I am well instructed in your ways, we will pursue our journey together."

The best of giants, in those days, were not scrupulous as to their mode of living, so that one of the best and one of the worst got on pretty well together, emptying the larders on the road, and paying nothing but douses on the chops. When they could find no inn, they hunted elephants and crocodiles. Morgante, who was the braver of the two, delighted to banter and sometimes to cheat Margutte, and he ate up all the fare, which made the other, notwithstanding the credit he gave himself for readiness of wit and tongue, cut a very sorry figure, and seriously remonstrate:

"I reverence you in other matters, but, in eating, you really do not behave well. He who deprives me of my share at meals is no friend; at every mouthful he robs me of, I seem to lose an eye. I am for dividing everything fairly, even if it be no more than a fig."

"You are a fine fellow," said Morgante; "you grow upon me very much."

So saying, he made him put some wood on the fire, and perform a hundred other offices to render everything snug; and then he went to sleep. Next day he cheated his great scoundrelly companion at drink, as he had done the day before at meat; and the poor, shabby devil complained; and Morgante laughed till he was nigh bursting, and continued to cheat him again and again. There was a levity, nevertheless, in Margutte which restored his spirits on the slightest glimpse of good fortune; and if he realized a hearty meal, he became the happiest, beastliest, and most confident of giants.

The companions, in the course of their journey, delivered a damsel from the clutches of three other giants. She was the daughter of a great lord, and when she got home she did honor to Morgante as an equal, and put Margutte into the kitchen, where he was in a state of bliss. He did nothing but swill, stuff, surfeit, vomit, play at dice, cheat, filch, go to sleep, guzzle again, and laugh, chatter, and tell a thousand lies.

When Morgante took leave of the young lady, she made him rich presents. Margutte, seeing this, and being, as usual, drunk and impudent, daubed his face like a Christmas clown, and, approaching her with a frying-pan in his hand, demanded "something for the cook." The fair one gave him a jewel; and the vagabond showed such brutal eagerness in seizing it with his filthy hands, without making the least acknowledgment, that when they got out of the house Morgante was tempted to strike him to the ground. He called him scoundrel and poltroon, and said he had disgraced him forever.

"Softly!" said the brute-beast. "Did you not take me with you knowing what sort of fellow I was? Did I not tell you I had every sin and shame under heaven? And have I ever deceived you by the exhibition of a single virtue?"

Morgante could not help laughing at this excessive candor. So they went on their way, till they came to a wood, where they rested themselves by a fountain. Here Margutte fell fast asleep. He had a pair of boots on, which Morgante felt an inclination to draw off, that he might see what he would do on waking. He accordingly did so, and threw them to a little distance among the bushes. The sleeper awoke in due time, and, looking and searching round about, suddenly burst into roars of laughter. A monkey had got the boots and sat pulling them on and off, making the most ridiculous grimaces and gestures. The monkey busied himself with the boots, and the light-minded drunkard laughed; and at every fresh gesticulation of the new boot-wearer the laugh grew louder and more tremendous, till at length it was found impossible to restrain it. The glutton had a laughing fit. In vain did he try to stop himself; in vain would his fingers have loosened the buttons of his doublet, to give his lungs room to play. They could not do it; so he laughed and roared till he burst. The snap was like the splitting of a cannon. Morgante ran up to him. But it was too late. He was dead.

Alas! this was not the only death. It was not even the most trivial cause of a death. Giants are big fellows; but Death's a bigger, though he may come in a little shape.

Morgante had succeeded in joining his master. He helped him to take Babylon; he killed a whale for him at sea that obstructed his passage; he played the part of a mainsail during a storm, holding out his arms with a large hide between them. But, on coming ashore, a crab bit him in the heel, and behold the lot of the great giant—he died! He laughed, and thought it a very little thing; but it proved a mighty one. "He made the East tremble," said his master, "and the bite of a crab has killed him."

Oh, weak, fallacious life of ours!

—"*Morgante the Great*" (*Leigh Hunt's Transcription*).

Masuccio di Salerno

The Inheritance of a Library

JERONIMO, who had inherited the place of master and head of the house, found himself in possession of many thousand florins in ready money. Wherefore the youth, seeing that he himself had endured no labor and weariness in gathering together the same, forthwith made up his mind not to place his affection in possessions of this sort, and at once began to array himself in sumptuous garments, to taste the pleasures of the town in the company of certain chosen companions of his, to indulge in amorous adventures, and in a thousand other ways to dissipate his substance abroad without restraint of any kind. Not only did he banish from his mind all thought and design of continuing his studies, but he even went so far as to harbor against the books, which his father had held in such high esteem and reverence and had bequeathed to him, the most fierce and savage hatred. So violent, indeed, was his resentment against them that he set them down as the worst foes he had in the world.

On a certain day it happened that the young man, either by accident or for some reason of his own, betook himself into the library of his dead father, and there his eye fell upon a vast quantity of handsome and well-arranged books, such as are wont to be found in places of this sort. At the first sight of these he was somewhat stricken with fear, and with a certain apprehension that the spirit of his father might pursue him; but, having collected his courage somewhat, he turned with a look of hatred on his face toward the aforesaid books and began to address them in the following terms:

"Books, books, so long as my father was alive you waged against me war unceasing, forasmuch as he spent all his time and trouble either in purchasing you, or in putting you in fair bindings; so that, whenever it might happen that there came upon me the need of a few florins or of certain other articles, which all youths find necessary, he would always refuse to let me have them, saying that it was his will and pleasure to dispense his money only in the purchase of such books as might please him. And over and beyond this, he purposed in his mind that I, altogether against my will, should spend my life in close companionship with you, and over this matter there arose between us many times angry and contumelious words. Many times, also, you have put me in danger of being driven into perpetual exile from this my home. Therefore it cannot but be pleasing to God—since it is no fault of yours that I was not hunted forth from this place—that I should send you packing from this my house in such fashion that not a single one of you will ever behold my door again. And, in sooth, I wonder more especially that you have not before this disordered my wits, a feat you might well have accomplished with very little more trouble on your part, in your desire to do with me as you did with my father, according to my clear recollection. He, poor man, as if he had become bemused through conversing with you alone, was accustomed to demean himself in strange fashion, moving his hands and his head in such wise that over and over again I counted him to be one bereft of reason. Now, on account of all this, I bid you have a little patience, for the reason that I have made up my mind to sell you all forthwith, and thus in a single hour to avenge myself for all the outrages I have suffered on your account and, over and beyond this, to set myself free from the possible danger of going mad."

After he had thus spoken, and had packed up divers volumes of the aforesaid books—one of his servants helping him in the work—he sent the parcel to the house of a certain lawyer, who was a friend of his, and then in a very few words came to an agreement with the lawyer as to the business, the issue of the affair being that, though he had simply expelled the books from his house, and had not sold them, he received, nevertheless, on account of the same, several hundred florins. With these, added to the money which still remained in his purse, he continued to pursue the course of pleasure he had begun.

—*The Collection of Tales, or " Novellino."*

The Silver Cup and the Lamprey

MASTER FLORIANO DA CASTEL SAN PIERO was known in his own day, among the people of Bologna, as a most famous and excellent doctor of laws. After he had come out of church one morning, he was walking up and down the great square of the city with certain other doctors of law, his friends, and in passing it chanced that he entered the shop of a silversmith living in those parts to whom he had given orders to make for him a rich and beautiful cup of silver gilt, and before he went any farther, and without holding any other discourse with the silversmith thereanent, he made out his account with the craftsman and paid it. Then, when he turned round to call his servant and bid him take the cup home, he found that the varlet was not there; so he begged the silversmith that he would as a favor send the cup to his house by the hand of his apprentice, which the silversmith undertook willingly to do.

Now at that time there were in Bologna two young men from the Roman states, who had come from the parts round about Trevi. These two were wandering through Italy from one place to another, carrying with them a store of false money and loaded dice and a thousand other crafty beguilements wherewith to defraud whomsoever they might meet, contriving the while to eat and drink and live a merry life by sponging upon others. Of these, one was named Liello di Cecco, and the other Andreuccio di Vallemontone; and these two, finding themselves by chance in the great piazza at that very same time when Master Floriano had bidden the silversmith let despatch the cup to his house, forthwith proposed one to the other to make an attempt to get this cup into their hands when they heard what orders had been given about it. It happened that they knew quite well the house where the doctor lived; and as soon as they perceived that the apprentice had come back from the discharge of his errand, Liello straightway gave command to his companion as to what course they must follow. First he betook himself to a tavern, and, after he had bought a very fine lamprey from a heap of large ones which was lying there, and hidden the same carefully beneath his mantle, he hurried at full speed to the house of Master Floriano. Then, having knocked at the door, he asked for the mistress of the house, and when he had been brought into her presence he said:

"Madam, your husband sends you this fish, and bids me tell you to have it daintily prepared at once for the table, as he is minded to dine here to-day with certain other doctors who are friends of his; and, moreover, he told me that you were to send back to him the same cup which the apprentice of the shop brought to you a little time ago, for the reason that he finds he has made an unprofitable bargain with the master silversmith, and wishes to have it taken back to the shop in order that it may be weighed again."

The simple woman, lending easy belief to the knave's words, immediately handed over to Liello the cup, and commanded her maid servants to lose no time in preparing the fish; and, having duly set in order such apparel as was needful for the reception of strangers at dinner, she awaited their coming with no little pleasure. Liello, as soon as he had got the cup safely in his possession, quickly made his way toward the monastery of San Michele in Bosco, where there dwelt a prior who was a Roman and a friend of the two sharpers, and an artist no less skilled in knavery than they themselves. This man gave Liello a friendly reception, and when he had heard the whole story, they both made merry over the good stroke which had been played, while they awaited the coming of Andreuccio, who had tarried behind in the square to listen to whatever might be said concerning the deed they had just wrought.

When the dinner hour had come Master Floriano, having taken leave of his companions, went to his house, and as he drew nigh thereto, his wife, observing that he was alone, went toward him and said:

"Sir, where are the guests you have invited?"

The doctor, greatly amazed at such a question as this, made answer to her, "What guests are these concerning whom you ask?"

"Know you not what guests I mean?" said the wife. "I,

for my part, have prepared everything for dinner in very handsome fashion."

Master Floriano, now more astonished than ever, cried out, "It seems to me that you must have lost your wits this morning."

Then said the wife, "Nay, I am well assured that my wits fail me not at all. You, in sooth, sent me a fine lamprey, with directions for me to get the same ready, seeing that you intended to bring hither with you several other doctors to dinner; and all the things you ordered me to do by your message I have done, and I hope these may be to your pleasure, otherwise we shall have lost our time and our trouble in no small measure."

The husband replied, "Certes, my wife, I do not comprehend the meaning of what you are saying, but may God ever go on sending to us people who use us in this kindly fashion —people who bring us something out of their own store without taking away in turn aught from ours. This time, in sooth, we must have been mistaken for some one else."

Now when the wife, who with such scant caution had handed over the cup to the knave, heard that in truth her husband knew nothing at all about the matter, she said, with her mind greatly disturbed:

"Sir, in my opinion it is exactly the opposite to what you say, forasmuch as the man who brought hither the fish asked me in your name to hand over to him the silver cup which the apprentice of the shop had brought here only a short time before, and he described to me so exactly all the marks thereof that I handed it over to him forthwith."

When Master Floriano heard that the cup had thus been cozened away from him, he understood at once that he had lost it by means of treacherous dealing; wherefore he cried out, "Ah, senseless numskull that you are! You have in sooth allowed yourself to be nicely tricked."

Then he departed straightway out of the house, and when he had come to the square he went searching about on every side without knowing why, demanding of every one he met if any man had been seen going in the direction of his house and carrying in his hand a fish. In fact, the doctor gave vent to a thousand other crazy humors without getting any good therefrom. He went from place to place playing the fool and sending people to the four winds, asking all sorts of questions bearing upon the business in hand, and sometimes trying to believe, with faint hope, that it was only a harmless trick which some one had played him.

In the meantime Andreuccio was standing at the corner of the square with all the outward seeming of a man of good repute, and although he deemed that by this time his comrade and the cup as well must have gained a harbor of refuge, he felt nevertheless no little vexation that he himself should have lost the good round sum he had spent in the purchase of the lamprey without ever tasting a mouthful of the same. Wherefore he made up his mind to get into his possession the lamprey by means of another trick no less astute than the first. Thus, taking advantage of the time when he perceived that Master Floriano was most hotly engaged in his search for the cup, he betook himself at the top of his speed to the doctor's house, and mounting the steps with a joyful face, he said to the wife:

"Madam, I bring to you good news, forasmuch as your husband has found the cup which certain friends of his caused to be stolen from him by way of playing a jest with him, therefore he has sent me hither to fetch the fish which you have got in order, and to take it to him, seeing that he is minded to make good cheer with the same in the company of those who snatched the cup out of his sight."

The wife, who had been overwhelmed with grief and trouble for the reason that she had been the cause of the loss of the cup, rejoiced mightily when she heard that it had been found; and having taken two large dishes of pewter, with a white and scented table-cloth, she placed the well-dressed fish within, and, glad at heart at the turn of affairs, she delivered it into the hands of the worthy Andreuccio. And he, as soon as he was clear of the house, wrapped up everything carefully under his cloak and flew as fast as his legs could carry him toward San Michele; and having arrived there, he met the prior and Liello, and the three held high revel over the excellent lamprey, laughing and jesting the while heartily. They afterward handed over the pewter dishes to the prior, and then, using the greatest cunning, they sold the cup and went their way to another place without raising any hue and cry with regard to their exploit.

Master Floriano, who had spent the whole of the day in vainly seeking to get some intelligence as to the matter, went back to his house late at night hungry and sorely out of humor; whereupon his wife, going forward to meet him, addressed him in these words:

"Glory be to God! seeing that by His help you have at last found the cup, through losing which I was called a numskull."

But he, with a heart filled with cruel resentment, replied: "Get out of my sight, conceited fool that you are! You do not wish to know what bad luck really is; for it appears that, over and beyond working a grievous wrong and injury to me by reason of your brutish folly, you now are minded to make a mock of me."

The wife, utterly confounded by what she heard, answered, all trembling with fear:

"Sir, in good faith I do not mean to jeer at you," and then she went on to tell him all about the second trick which had been put upon her.

Master Floriano, when he heard this, fell into a humor so overwrought and grief-stricken that he came little short of losing his wits entirely; and after he had spent a great deal of time and tried every scheme, with all sorts of most subtle investigations, to lay his hands on the thieves, he lived for a long season with his wife in sore hatred and ill-will, having failed altogether to discover anything about those who had duped him. And in this fashion the Romans enjoyed the fruit of their cunning deceit, and left the doctor, tricked and flouted, with his sorrow and loss.

—*The Collection of Tales, or " Novellino."*

Francesco Berni

Living in Bed

Yet field-sports, dice, cards, balls, and such like courses,
  Things which he might be thought to set store by,
Gave him but little pleasure. He liked horses,
  But was content to let them please his eye—
Buying them, not squaring with his resources.
  Therefore his *summum bonum* was to lie
Stretch'd at full length—yea, frankly be it said,
To do no single thing but lie in bed.

'Twas owing all to that infernal writing.
  Body and brains had borne such grievous rounds
Of kicks, cuffs, floors, from copying and inditing,
  That he could find no balsam for his wounds,
No harbor for his wreck half so inviting
  As to lie still, far from all sights and sounds,
And so, in bed, do nothing on God's earth
But try and give his senses a new birth.

"Bed—bed's the thing, by Heaven!" thus would he swear.
  "Bed is your only work, your only duty.
Bed is one's gown, one's slippers, one's armchair,
  Old coat; you're not afraid to spoil its beauty.
Large you may have it, long, wide, brown, or fair,
  Down-bed or mattress, just as it may suit ye.
Then take your clothes off, turn in, stretch, lie double;
Be but in bed, you're quit of earthly trouble!"

Borne to the fairy palace then, but tired
  Of seeing so much dancing, he withdrew
Into a distant room, and there desired
  A bed might be set up, handsome and new,
With all the comforts that the case required:
  Mattresses huge, and pillows not a few
Put here and there, in order that no ease
Might be found wanting to cheeks, or arms, or knees.

The bed was eight feet wide, lovely to see,
  With white sheets, and fine curtains, and rich loops—
Things vastly soothing to calamity;
  The coverlet hung light in silken droops;
It might have held six people easily;
  But he disliked to lie in bed by groups.
A large bed to himself, that was his notion,
With room enough to swim in—like the ocean.

In this retreat there joined him a good soul,
  A Frenchman, one who had been long at court,
An admirable cook—though, on the whole,
  His gains of his deserts had fallen short.
For him was made, cheek, as it were, by jowl,
  A second bed of the same noble sort,
Yet not so close but that the folks were able
To set between the two a dinner-table.

Here was served up, on snow-white table-cloths,
  Each daintiest procurable comestible
In the French taste (all others being Goths),
  Dishes alike delightful and digestible.

Only our scribe chose sirups, soups, and broths,
   The smallest trouble being a detestable
Bore, into which not ev'n his dinner led him.
Therefore the servants always came and fed him.

Nothing at these times but his head was seen;
   The coverlet came close beneath his chin;
And then, from out the bottle or tureen,
   They fill'd a silver pipe, which he let in
Between his lips, all easy, smooth, and clean,
   And so he filled his philosophic skin.
And not a finger all the while he stirred,
Nor, lest his tongue should tire, scarce uttered word.

The name of that same cook was Master Pierre;
   He told a tale well—something short and light.
Quoth scribe, "Those people who keep dancing there
   Have little wit." Quoth Pierre, "You're very right."
And then he told a tale, or hummed an air;
   Then took a sip of something, or a bite;
And then he turned himself to sleep; and then
Awoke and ate. And then he slept again.

   .   .   .   .   .

One more thing I may note that made the day
   Pass well—one custom, not a little healing,
Which was, to look above him, as he lay,
   And count the spots and blotches in the ceiling;
Noting what shapes they took to, and which way,
   And where the plaster threatened to be peeling;
Whether the spot looked new, or old, or what—
Or whether 'twas, in fact, a spot or not.
                            —*"Roland Enamored."*

Lodovico Ariosto

What Astolfo Saw in the Moon

AFTER Astolfo and Saint John had spent two days in discourse, during which meals had been served up consisting of fruit so exquisite that the paladin could not help thinking our first parents had some excuse for eating it, the evangelist, when the moon rose, took him into the car which had borne Elijah to heaven; and four horses redder than fire conveyed them to the lunar world.

The mortal visitant was amazed to see in the moon a world resembling his own, full of wood and water, and containing even cities and castles, though of a different sort from ours. It was strange to find a sphere so large which had seemed so petty afar off; and no less strange was it to look down on the world he had left and be compelled to knit his brows and look sharply before he could well discern it, for it happened at the time to be in want of light.

But his guide did not leave him much time to look about. He conducted him with due speed to a valley which contained, in one miraculous collection, whatsoever had been lost or wasted on earth—not only riches and dominions and such like gifts of fortune, but things also which fortune can neither grant nor resume. Much fame is there which time has withdrawn, infinite prayers and vows which are made to God Almighty by us poor sinners. There lie the tears and the sighs of lovers, the hours lost in play, the leisures of the dull, and the intentions of the lazy. As to desires, they are so numerous that they shadow the whole place. Astolfo went round among the different heaps, asking what they were. His eyes were first struck with a huge one of bladders, which seemed to contain mighty sounds and the voices of multitudes, and which he was told were the Assyrian and Persian monarchies, together with those of Greece and Lydia. One heap was nothing but hooks of silver and gold, which were the presents, it seems, made to patrons and great men in hopes of a return. Another consisted of snares in the shape of garlands, manufactured by parasites. Others were verses in praise of great lords, all made of crickets which had burst themselves with singing. Chains of gold he saw there which were fictitious and unhappy love-matches; and eagles' claws, which were deputed authorities; and pairs of bellows, which were princes' favors; and overturned cities and treasuries, being treasons and conspiracies; and serpents with female faces, that were coiners and thieves; and all sorts of broken bottles, which were services rendered in miserable courts. A great heap of overturned soup he found to be alms to the poor, which had been delayed till the giver's death. Heaps of twigs he saw, set with birdlime, which, dear ladies, are your charms. In short, there was no end to what he saw. Thousands and thousands would not complete the list. Everything was there which was to be met with on earth, except folly in the raw material, for that is never exported. There he beheld some of his own lost time and deeds, and yet, if nobody had been with him to make him aware of them, never would he have recognized them as his.

They then arrived at something which none of us ever prayed God to bestow, for we fancy we possess it in superabundance; yet here it was in greater quantities than anything else in the place—I mean, sense. It was a subtle fluid, apt to evaporate if not kept closely, and here, accordingly, it was kept in vials of greater or less size. The greatest of them all was inscribed with the following words, " The Sense of Roland." Others in like manner exhibited the names of the proper possessors; and among them the frankhearted paladin beheld the larger portion of his own. But what astonished him more was to see multitudes of the vials almost full to the stopper, which bore the names of men whom he had supposed to enjoy their senses in perfection. Some had lost them for love, others for glory, others for riches, others for promises from great men, others for stupid tricks, for jewels, for paintings, for all sorts of whims. There was a heap belonging to sophists and astrologers, and a still greater to poets.

Astolfo, with leave of Saint John, took possession of his own. He had but to uncork it and put it under his nose, and the wit shot up to its place at once. For a long time afterward the paladin led the life of a wise man, until, unfortunately, a mistake which he made lost him his brains a second time.

The evangelist now presented him with the vial containing the wits of Roland, and the travelers quitted the vale of lost treasures.

" Raving Roland " (*Leigh Hunt's Transcription*).

Matteo Bandello

Of a Trick Played upon Some Monks by a Donkey

You must know that in the venerable convent of San Do-
menico, at Modena, Brother Agostino Moro being prior at
that time, as doubtless you are aware, there happened to be
an excellent preacher on the third day of Easter. All through
Lent he had preached to the general satisfaction of the whole
city, and was now about to take leave of his congregation
with such rites and ceremonies as preachers commonly adopt.
When it got about that this was the father's farewell sermon, all folk flocked to the church, so that it seemed as if the
day were one of plenary indulgence. So hot and stifling had
the church become with the crowd and the breath of so many
men and women, that when the sermon was over—it had
lasted from dinner-time to four o'clock—the friars found it
passing difficult to chant vespers and compline together. Being a shrewd and thoughtful person, the sacristan opened all
the doors and windows of the church to cool the air, waiting
as long as he could before closing the great door, especially
as at nightfall they were to bury there a man of very foul
reputation, to whom, when dying, as all averred, the devil
had appeared in the flesh, so that they thought he would be
carried away, soul and body. When the funeral rites for
this arch-sinner were ended, the sacristan closed the central
door of the church, but left the one leading to the first clois-

35

ter open, so that the church might grow cooler during the night.

That same evening a friar arrived who had been preaching in the mountains, and brought his baggage with him upon a little ass as black as pitch, which he put up in a stable hard by. But, while all slept, the donkey, I know not how, got out of the stable and strayed into the cloister, where the grass was rich and tender. Here it stopped for a while to eat its fill. Then, being thirsty perhaps, it went sniffing about till it spied the vessel containing holy water, and drank it all up, as the friars next day discovered. Having eaten and drunk, it approached the grave of the wicked man, which had been filled in with sand, and, after turning round several times, stretched itself out there to rest.

Now, at the first stroke of matins it is usual for novices to go to the choir and set books and candles in readiness for chanting the service. So, at the time stated, two boys came in to prepare all that was necessary, and, passing through the sacristy, they saw Master Jackass stretched out upon the grave. His eyes looked like two great burning coals, while his long ears seemed for all the world like a pair of horns. Darkness, that fosterer and ally of fear, the thought of the newly buried sinner, and the sight of so horrible a brute at such an hour, fairly robbed the poor timid lads of their senses, and they firmly believed that the beast was none other than the devil. So, in their terror, they fled as fast as their legs would carry them; and he who ran swiftest deemed himself very lucky. On reaching the dormitory, breathless and speechless, they met some of the friars going to the choir, among these being the master of the novices. Seeing, by the light that burns all night long in the dormitory, that the boys had come back, he asked them why they had not gone to prepare for matins, when in great fear and trembling they told him that on the grave of the man buried overnight they had actually seen the enemy of mankind.

The good monk, by no means the most courageous of men, began to tremble with fear, uncertain whether to go down into the church or not. Just then Brother Giovanni Mascarello came up, leader of the choir, and an excellent musician. Hearing the lads' story, he boldly ran down and went into the church. Here he saw the brute crouched on the grave, with ears erect because of the noise it heard, and quickly turning his back to it, he slammed the door of the sacristy and rushed up-stairs, screaming at the top of his voice, "Fathers, it is indeed the devil, the enemy of mankind." This he repeated again and again. As you know, he has a very powerful voice, and he shouted so loud that there was not a friar in the convent who did not hear him.

At last the prior came out of his cell, and, approaching Brother Giovanni, said, "What folly is this that you say? Are you raving mad, or what is it? Be still, and do not make such a noise at this hour. In God's name, what is the matter?"

"Holy father," replied Brother Giovanni, "I am not raving mad, but I tell you that the devil is in the church, and with my own eyes I actually saw him on the grave of that wicked man whom we buried yestereve. Methinks he has come to bear away the sinner's body with him to hell! These lads here have seen him also."

Having questioned the boys, who confirmed this statement, the prior, with some of the monks whom the outcry had brought thither, went down into the church. Their imaginations being excited by what they had heard, at the sight of the ass they all firmly believed that it was the Prince of Evil.

So, quaking with fear, each made the sign of the cross and went back to the sacristy, whereupon the prior, after brief consultation with the friars, had the big bell rung, which brought all the inmates of the monastery together, when he exhorted them to be of good courage and not to dread this devilish apparition. Emboldened by this speech, the friars went in a body to the sacristy, where they donned their sacred vestments, and took all the relics they possessed, so that each bore some holy thing in his hand. Then, the cross going before, they marched forth in procession, chanting with great fervor the *Salve Regina*. But Master Jackass remained completely at his ease through it all, never budging an inch from his self-chosen position. Few of the friars were brave enough to look at the brute, being firmly convinced that it was the devil, while none of them had the least idea that it was a donkey. When the *Salve Regina* had been sung and the beast showed no signs of moving, the prior called for the book of exorcisms, which is used to drive out evil spirits from the bodies of those possessed, and he then read all those holy words which are meet in such emergencies; yet, for all this, master donkey never stirred.

At last the prior took the sprinkler used for holy water, and coming somewhat closer to the brute, he raised his hand, and making the sign of the cross, began to sprinkle holy water, never perceiving that the foul fiend of his imagination was none other than an ass. So he soused him soundly two or three times, when, either because the water was cold or because he thought the sprinkling stick would hit him—for he saw the prior continually raise his hand as if about to beat him—Master Neddy stood up on all-fours and brayed with hideous vigor. By this ludicrous signal he proved to the prior and the monks that he was not Satan, after all, but

an ass. The good friars were filled with confusion, not knowing what to say nor what to do. But the whole thing ended
in loud laughter, as it seemed to them a mighty joke that
young and old, philosophers and theologians, should one and
all have been thus mocked by an ass.

Benvenuto Cellini

A Lawsuit and Some Domestic Vicissitudes

AFTER I had got rid of my Frenchman, I found myself obliged to proceed in the same manner with another tradesman, but did not demolish the house. I only caused the goods to be thrown out of the window. . . .

The second person whom I had driven out of the precincts of my castle commenced a lawsuit against me at Paris, affirming that I had robbed him of several of his effects at the time that I dislodged him. This suit occasioned me a great deal of trouble, and took up so much of my time that I was frequently upon the point of forming a desperate resolution to quit the kingdom. It is customary in France to make the most of a suit which they commence with a foreigner, or with any other person who is not used to law transactions; as soon as they have any advantage in the process, they find means to sell it to certain persons who make a trade of buying lawsuits. There is another villainous practise which is general with the Normans; I mean that of bearing false witness; so that those who purchase the suit immediately instruct five or six of these witnesses, as there happens to be occasion. By such means, if their adversary cannot produce an equal number to contradict and destroy their evidence, and happens to be ignorant of the custom of the country, he is sure to have a decree given against him.

Both these accidents having happened to me, I thought the proceeding highly dishonorable. I therefore made my appearance in the great hall of the Court of Justice at Paris in order to plead my own cause, where I saw the king's lieutenant for civil affairs seated upon a grand tribunal. This man was tall, corpulent, and had a most austere countenance. On one side he was surrounded by a multitude of people, and on the other with numbers of attorneys and counselors, all ranged in order upon the right and left; others came, one by one, and severally opened their causes before the judge. I observed that the counselors, who stood on one side, sometimes spoke all together. To my great surprise, this extraordinary magistrate, with the true countenance of a Plato, seemed by his attitude to listen now to one, now to another, and constantly answered with the utmost propriety. As I always took great pleasure in seeing and contemplating the efforts of genius, of what nature soever, this appeared to me so wonderful that I would not have missed seeing it for any consideration. As the hall was of a prodigious extent, and filled with a great multitude of persons, particular care was taken that none should enter but such as came about business; so the door was kept locked, and the avenues were guarded by doorkeepers. These men, in opposing those who were for forcing in, sometimes made such a noise that the judge reprimanded them very severely. I stooped down several times to observe what passed. The words which I heard the judge utter, upon seeing two gentlemen who wanted to hear the trial, and whom the porter was endeavoring to keep out, were these, " Be quiet, be quiet, Satan, get hence, and leave off disturbing us!" The terms in French were, *Paix, paix, Satan, allez, paix!* As I had by this time thoroughly learned the French language, upon hearing these words I recollected what Dante said, when he and his master, Vergil, entered the gates of hell; for Dante and Giotto, the painter, were together in France, and visited Paris with particular attention, where the Court of Justice may be considered as hell. Hence it is that Dante, who was likewise perfect master of the French, made use of that expression; and I have often been surprised that it was never understood in that sense; so that I cannot help thinking that the commentators on this author have often made him say things which he never so much as dreamed of.

To return to my suit. I found that when verdicts were given against me, and there was no redress to be expected from the law, I must have recourse to a long sword, which I had by me, for I was always particularly careful to be provided with good arms. The first I attacked was the person who commenced that unjust and vexatious suit; and one evening I gave him so many wounds upon the legs and arms, taking care, however, not to kill him, that I deprived him of the use of both his legs. I then fell upon the other, who had bought the cause, and treated him in such a manner as quickly caused a stop to be put to the proceedings. For this, and every other success, I returned thanks to the Supreme Being, and began to conceive hopes that I should be for some time unmolested. I earnestly entreated my young journeymen, especially the Italians, to be attentive to their business, and to work hard for a time, till I could finish the works I had undertaken. For I proposed to return to Italy as soon as ever they were completed, not being able any longer to bear the villainy of the French; at the same time seriously considering that, if the monarch should once happen to be angry with me, I might probably meet with severe treatment for having revenged myself in the manner I had done.

These Italian journeymen were as follows:

The first and highest in my favor was Ascanio, born in the kingdom of Naples, at a place called Tagliacozzo. The second was Paolo, a Roman, a person of mean birth, who did not so much as know his own father. These two I had brought from Rome, where they had lived with me. The third was likewise a Roman, who came from Italy on purpose to enter into my service. His name was also Paolo, and he was son to a poor Roman gentleman of the Maccherani family. This young man had made but little proficiency in the business, but he was brave, and an excellent swordsman. The fourth journeyman was a native of Ferrara, whose name was Bartolomeo Chioccia. The fifth was a Florentine, named Paolo Micceri, who had a brother, surnamed Gatta, a very able clerk, but guilty of extravagance when he managed the business for Tommasso Guadagni, a rich merchant. He afterward kept my books, which contained my accounts with his most Christian Majesty, and others by whom I was employed.

Paolo Micceri, having learned his brother's method of bookkeeping, continued to follow it, and I allowed him a good salary. He appeared to me to be a very pious youth, and discovered a great turn to devotion, sometimes singing psalms, sometimes telling his beads, so that I conceived great hopes from such an appearance of virtue. I therefore called him aside and spoke to him thus:

"My dear friend Paolo, you see how happily you are settled with me, and may remember you were before out of business. You are a Florentine, which makes me confide in you; and what gives me high satisfaction is to see you so pious, and so regular in all acts of religion. I therefore, putting more trust in you than in the others, make it my request to you that you would give your attention to two things, in which I am in a particular manner concerned. One is, that you would carefully watch over my property, and be always upon your guard to prevent anybody from meddling with it, as likewise that you avoid touching it yourself. At the same time you see the poor girl Caterina, whom I keep in the house chiefly on account of my business, and without whom it would be impossible for me to conduct it. Now I have particular reasons for wishing that she should be extremely circumspect in her conduct; therefore I desire you to watch her attentively, and inform me of any improprieties you may observe. I have no desire to provide for other people's children, nor would I tamely put up with such a thing. Were I to detect so scandalous an outrage, I would sacrifice both to my insulted honor. Therefore be prudent, and obey my injunctions; let me know if you observe anything wrong, and I will dismiss both her and her mother with disgrace."

This traitor crossed himself from head to foot, and made the most solemn asseverations that such an idea as that of injuring so great a benefactor in the smallest particular could never enter his mind. His appeals to all that was sacred, and apparent devotion to me, completely imposed upon me.

Two days afterward my countryman Maltio de Nasaro invited me and all my establishment to partake of his hospitality at his country house. When I proposed to take Paolo with me to enjoy himself, he observed how dangerous it would be to leave the house unprotected, and such gold, silver, and jewels lying all about, and that there were thieves on the lookout day and night. " Go, then, and enjoy yourself, dear master," he added, " and I will keep watch." So, taking Ascanio and Chioccia with me, I set out and spent the greater part of the day with infinite satisfaction. But toward evening I began to feel uncomfortable and out of humor. The words used by Paolo kept recurring to my mind. I could not master my uneasiness, and at last I took horse, and with two of my attendants returned to my castle. I had very nearly taken the villain by surprise; for as I entered the court I heard the wretch of a mother crying:

"Paolo! Caterina! here is the master!"

Soon they both appeared, terror and confusion depicted in every feature, scarcely knowing what they said or did, and evidently guilty. Overpowered by momentary rage, I seized my sword, resolved to kill them upon the spot. One fled, the other fell at my feet beseeching mercy, a movement that allowed me time to recover my reason. I determined then to turn them both out of the place. Turning to Paolo, I exclaimed:

"Thou basest of wretches, had my eyes been a little sharper, I would have passed this weapon through thy craven heart. Now thank thy stars, and get up and away." And with every opprobrious epithet, cuffs, and kicks, I chased both mother and daughter out of my castle.

In conjunction with a low attorney, a Norman, these wretches entered into a foul conspiracy against me, which caused me the greatest uneasiness, and compelled me to seek redress in a court of justice. Thus, the more I sought for peace to pursue my occupations, the more I encountered tribulation, as if Fortune were bent on finding new modes of persecuting me. I began to think of adopting one of two alternatives, either to quit France altogether or to exhaust her full vengeance, and see what strange destiny Heaven had yet in store for me. I persevered, and, having threatened to appeal to the king, my enemies took the alarm, and I came off victorious out of this fresh sea of troubles. By meeting it manfully I cleared my character and saved five hundred crowns, the forfeit of my non-appearance in the court. So, returning thanks to God, I returned joyfully to my castle, with my young assistants, who had appeared in my behalf.

—*The " Biography."*

A Compulsory Marriage at Sword's Point

ONE of those busy personages who delight in spreading mischief came to inform me that Paolo Micceri had taken a house for his new lady and her mother, and that he made use of the most injurious and contemptuous expressions regarding me, to wit:

" Poor Benvenuto! he paid the piper while I danced; and now he goes about boasting of the exploit. He thinks I am afraid of him—I, who can wear a sword and dagger as well as he. But I would have him to know my weapons are as keen as his. I, too, am a Florentine, and come of the Micceri, a much better house than the Cellini any time of day."

In short, the vile informer painted the things in such colors to my disadvantage that it fired my whole blood. I was in a fever of the most dangerous kind. And feeling it must kill me unless it found vent, I had recourse to my usual means on such occasions. I called to my workman, Chioccia, to accompany me, and told another to follow me with my horse. On reaching the wretch's house, finding the door half open, I entered abruptly in. There he sat with his precious " lady-love," his boasted sword and dagger beside him, in the very act of jesting with the elder woman upon my affairs. To slam the door, draw my sword and present the point to

46

his throat, was the work of a moment, giving him no time to think of defending himself:

"Vile poltroon, recommend thy soul to God! Thou art a dead man!"

In the excess of his terror he cried out thrice, in a feeble voice, "Mama! mama! mama! Help, help, help!"

At this ludicrous appeal, so like a girl's, and the ridiculous manner in which it was uttered, though I had a mind to kill, I lost half my rage and could not forbear laughing. Turning to Chioccia, however, I bade him make fast the door; for I was resolved to inflict the same punishment upon all three. Still with my sword-point at his throat, and pricking him a little now and then, I terrified him with the most desperate threats, and finding that he made no defense, was rather at a loss how to proceed. It was too poor a revenge—it was nothing—when suddenly it came into my head to make it effectual, and compel him to espouse the girl upon the spot.

"Up! Off with that ring on thy finger, villain!" I cried. "Marry her this instant, and then I shall have my full revenge."

"Anything—anything you like, provided you will not kill me," he eagerly answered.

Removing my sword a little:

"Now, then," I said, "put on the ring."

He did so, trembling all the time.

"This is not enough. Go and bring me two notaries to draw up the contract." Then, addressing the girl and her mother in French:

"While the notaries and witnesses are coming, I will give you a word of advice. The first of you that I know to utter a word about my affairs, I will kill you—all three. So remember."

I afterward said in Italian to Paolo:

" If you offer the slightest opposition to the least thing I choose to propose, I will cut you up into mince-meat with this good sword."

" It is enough," he interrupted in alarm, " that you will not kill me. I will do whatever you wish."

So this singular contract was duly drawn out and signed. My rage and fever were gone. I paid the notaries, and went home.—*The " Biography."*

Criticism of a Statue of Hercules

BANDINELLO was incensed to such a degree that he was ready to burst with fury, and turning to me said, " What faults have you to find with my statues?"

I answered, " I will soon tell them, if you have but the patience to hear me."

He replied, " Tell them, then."

The duke and all present listened with the utmost attention. I began by premising that I was sorry to be obliged to lay before him all the blemishes of his work, and that I was not so properly delivering my own sentiments as declaring what was said of it by the artistic school of Florence. However, as the fellow at one time said something disobliging, at another made some offensive gesture with his hands or his feet, he put me into such a passion that I behaved with a rudeness which I should otherwise have avoided.

" The artistic school of Florence," said I, " declares what follows: If the hair of your Hercules were shaved off, there would not remain skull enough to hold his brains.

With regard to his face, it is hard to distinguish whether it be the face of a man, or that of a creature something between a lion and an ox; it discovers no attention to what it is about; and it is so ill set upon the neck, with so little art and in so ungraceful a manner, that a more shocking piece of work was never seen. His great brawny shoulders resemble the two pommels of an ass's pack-saddle. His breasts and their muscles bear no similitude to those of a man, but seem to have been drawn from a sack of melons. As he leans directly against the wall, the small of the back has the appearance of a bag filled with long cucumbers. It is impossible to conceive in what manner the two legs are fastened to this distorted figure, for it is hard to distinguish upon which leg he stands, or upon which he exerts any effort of his strength; nor does he appear to stand upon both, as he is sometimes represented by those masters of the art of statuary who know something of their business. It is plain, too, that the statue inclines more than one-third of a cubit forward; and this is the greatest and the most insupportable blunder which pretenders to sculpture can be guilty of. As for the arms, they both hang down in the most awkward and ungraceful manner imaginable; and so little art is displayed in them that people would be almost tempted to think that you had never seen a naked man in your life. The right leg of Hercules and that of Cacus touch at the middle of their calves, and if they were to be separated, not one of them only, but both, would remain without a calf in the place where they touch. Besides, one of the feet of the Hercules is quite buried, and the other looks as if it stood upon hot coals."—*The "Biography."*

Giovanni Della Casa

Call Me Not John!

WERE I some fifteen years, or twenty, less,
Master Gandolfo, I'd unbaptize myself,
On purpose not to be called John. I ne'er
Can do a single thing by way of business,
Nor set out fast enough from my own door,
But half a dozen folk are calling after me;
Though, when I turn, it isn't me—such crowds
Named John are issuing forth at that same moment;
'Tis downright insult, a real public scandal.
Clergymen, lawyers, pedants—not a soul
But his name's John. You shall not see a face
Looking like what it is, a simpleton's—
Barber's, porkman's, or tooth-drawer's—but the fellow
Seems by his look to be a John—and is one!
I do believe that the first man who cried
Boiled apples—yes, or macaroni—was a John;
And so was he who found out roasted chestnuts,
And how to eat cucumbers, and new cheese.
By Heaven! I'd rather be a German; nay, a Jew,
And be called Matthew, or Bartholomew,
Or some such beast—or Simon. Really, people
Who christen people ought to pause a little,
And think what they're about. Oh, you who love me,
Don't call me John, for God's sake! Or, at least,
If you must call me so, oh, do it softly!
For, as to mentioning that name out loud,

Giovanni Della Casa

You might as well call to one like a dog,
Whistle, and snap your fingers, and cry, " Here, boy ! "
Think of the name upon a title-page !
It damns the book at once, and reasonably :
People no sooner see it than conclude
They've read the work before. Oh, I must say
My father made a pretty business of it,
Calling me John—me, faith ! his eldest son,
Heir to his poverty ! Why, there's not a writ,
But nine times out of ten is served on John,
And, what still more annoys me, not a bill :
Your promiser to pay is always John.
Some people fondly make the word a compound,
And get some other name to stand its friend,
Christening the hapless wight John-Antony,
John-Peter, or John-Baptist, or John-Charles;
There's even John-Bernard, John-Martin, and John-Richard.
Oh, ask if t'other name likes such society !
It never does, humor it as you will.
Change it, diminish it, call it Johnny, Jacky,
Jack : 'tis always a sore point—a wound—
Shocking if left alone, and worse if touched.

Francesco Redi

Diatribe Against Water

HE who drinks water,
I wish to observe,
Gets nothing from me;
He may eat it and starve.
Whether it's well, or whether it's fountain,
Or whether it comes foaming white from the mountain,
    I cannot admire it,
    Nor ever desire it.
'Tis a fool, and a madman, an impudent wretch,
Who now will live in a nasty ditch,
And then grows proud, and full of his whims,
Comes playing the devil, and cursing his brims,
And swells, and tumbles, and bothers his margins,
And ruins the flowers, although they be virgins.
Wharves and piers, were it not for him,
    Would last forever,
    If they're built clever;
But no, it's all one with him—sink or swim.

Let the people yclept Mameluke
Praise the Nile without any rebuke;
Let the Spaniards praise the Tagus;
I cannot like either, even for negus.
If any follower of mine
Dares so far to forget his wine

Francesco Redi

As to drink a drop of water,
Here's the hand to devote him to slaughter.
Let your meager doctorlings
Gather herbs and such like things,
Fellows who with streams and stills
Think to cure all sorts of ills;
I've no faith in their washery,
Nor think it worth a glance of my eye.
Yes, I laugh at them, for that matter,
To think how they, with their heaps of water,
Petrify their skulls profound,
And make 'em all so thick and so round,
That Viviana, with all his mathematics,
Would fail to square the circle of their attics.

Away with all water wherever I come;
I forbid it ye, gentlemen, all and some.
   Lemonade water,
   Jessamine water,
   Our tavern knows none of 'em—
   Water's a hum!
Jessamine makes a pretty crown,
But as a drink 'twill never go down.
All your hydromels and flips
Come not near these prudent lips.
All your sippings and sherbets,
And a thousand such pretty sweets,
Let your mincing ladies take 'em,
And fops whose little fingers ache 'em.
Wine, wine is your only drink!
Grief never dares to look at the brink.

Six times a year to be mad with wine,
I hold it no shame, but a very good sign.
I, for my part, take my can,
Solely to act like a gentleman,
And, acting so, I care not, I,
For all the hail and snow in the sky.
    I never go poking,
       And cowering and cloaking,
And wrapping myself from head to foot,
As some people do, with their wigs to boot—
For example, like dry and shivering Redi,
Who looks just like a peruk'd old lady.
          —*"Bacchus in Tuscany."*

Carlo Goldoni

Forcing a Match

GERONTE, *alone*.

Ger. Yes, Martuccia is right. I sometimes allow my temper to get the better of me. But I must treat my niece with the gentleness she deserves.

Enter ANGELICA, *who remains standing at the door.*

Ger. Come closer, niece.

Ang. (*advancing timidly*). Sir——

Ger. How do you expect me to hear you if you remain three miles away?

Ang. (*comes nearer, trembling*). Sir—I beg your pardon—I——

Ger. Well, what have you to say?

Ang. Has Martuccia told you nothing?

Ger. Yes, she spoke of you, and then of your brother—that erratic fellow—that idiot, who is letting a harebrained woman lead him by the nose, who has ruined himself, who is done for, for whom I have lost all respect! (ANGELICA *turns to go.*)

Ger. (*excitedly*). Where are you going?

Ang. Sir, you seem to be angry——

Ger. Well, what business is that of yours? If I get angry with a fool, how can that affect you? Come here, and speak to me. Never mind my being put out.

Ang. My dear uncle, I shall never dare to speak until you are in a calmer frame of mind.

Ger. (*aside*). This is unendurable! Well, I am calm now. Speak.

Ang. Martuccia may have told you——

Ger. I don't care a straw what Martuccia told me. I want to hear it from yourself.

Ang. (*timorously*). My brother——

Ger. (*mocking her*). Your brother——

Ang. Wants to shut me up in a convent.

Ger. Do you want to go to a convent?

Ang. Why, sir——

Ger. Answer at once!

Ang. It is not for me to decide.

Ger. I never asked you to decide! (*Furiously.*) I want to know what you think about it!

Ang. Oh, sir, you frighten me!

Ger. (*aside*). I am dying with rage! (*Restraining himself.*) Come here; I am listening. So the convent does not suit you?

Ang. No.

Ger. What would you prefer to do?

Ang. Sir, I——

Ger. Don't be afraid. I am perfectly calm. Speak freely.

Ang. Oh, I have not the courage!

Ger. Come here! Do you want to marry?

Ang. Sir——

Ger. Yes or no.

Ang. If you would only——

Ger. Yes or no.

Ang. Why, yes, I——

Ger. Yes, do you say? You want to marry? You want to throw away your liberty, your peace of mind? Very well, so much the worse for you. Yes, you shall marry.

Ang. (*aside*). He is really very kind in spite of his bad temper.

Ger. Have you any particular choice?

Ang. (*aside*). Oh! if I only had the courage to tell him about Valerio!

Ger. What! Do you mean to say you already have some lover?

Ang. (*aside*). I am sure this is not the right moment. I shall ask Martuccia to interview him.

Ger. Now, this is enough. Let us settle the question. The house where you live, the people you see, may perhaps have led you to form some attachment? Out with the truth! (*Angrily.*) Yes, I am going to do something for you, but only on condition that you deserve it. Do you hear?

Ang. (*very much frightened*). Ye-e-s.

Ger. Now, then, answer me openly, frankly: Is it the case that you have any preference?

Ang. Oh, no, sir—I—I have none.

Ger. So much the better. I will engage to find a husband for you.

Ang. Oh—sir—uncle—I had not——

Ger. What's the matter now?

Ang. You know how timid I am.

Ger. Yes, yes, I know all about your timidity. I know what women are. You are a turtle-dove now, but after you are married you will be a dragon.

Ang. Well, then, my dear uncle, as you are so kind——

Ger. Yes, too kind——

Ang. Let me confess to you——

Ger. Confound it, that fellow Dorval is not here yet!

Ang. Listen, my dear uncle——

Ger. Leave me alone! (*Turns to a chess-board with pieces standing on it.*)

Ang. Only a word!

Ger. No, that's enough!

Ang. (*aside*). Heavens! Here I am, unhappier than ever! But my dear Martuccia will not forsake me. (*Exit.*)

* * * * * *

GERONTE *and* DORVAL.

Ger. Let us finish our game of chess, and say no more about that affair.

Dor. But it is about your nephew——

Ger. About an idiot, a miserable creature who is the slave of his wife and the victim of his vanity!

Dor. Not so excited, my dear friend—not so excited!

Ger. Oh, you with your coolness, you drive me mad!

Dor. I am speaking to you with the best of intentions.

Ger. Sit down.

Dor. (*aside*). I am sorry for his poor nephew.

Ger. Now, let us see about this game we left off yester-day——

Dor. You will lose——

Ger. Perhaps not. Let us see.

Dor. I repeat, you will lose——

Ger. No, I feel quite sure——

Dor. If you do not come to his assistance, you will lose him altogether.

Ger. Lose what?

Dor. Your nephew.

Ger. Confound it! I was talking about the game. Sit down, I tell you!

Dor. I shall be very glad to play, only I want you to listen to me first.

Ger. Are you going to talk about that young Dalancour?

Dor. Perhaps I may.

Ger. Then I will not listen.

Dor. So you hate him?

Ger. No, sir, I hate no one.

Dor. But, if you will not——

Ger. That's enough. Play! If the game is not to be continued I shall go away.

Dor. Only a word, and I shall have done.

Ger. Heavens, how patient I am!

Dor. You have a considerable fortune.

Ger. Yes, the Lord be praised!

Dor. More than enough for your own wants——

Ger. Yes, enough to help my friends if necessary.

Dor. And still you decline to give anything to your nephew?

Ger. Not a farthing shall he have!

Dor. Consequently——

Ger. Consequently?

Dor. You hate him.

Ger. Consequently, you don't know what you are talking about. I detest, I loathe his way of thinking, his abominable conduct. To give him money would simply be to encourage his vanity, his extravagance, and his folly. Let him change his system, and I will change as soon as he does. I want to see beneficence deserved through repentance, and not repentance hindered by beneficence.

Dor. Very well, then. Let us go on with the game.

Ger. Yes, let us play.

Dor. (*makes a move*). I am very sorry for him——

Ger. (*makes a move*). Check to your king.

Dor. (*makes a move*). And that poor girl——

Ger. What girl?

Dor. Your niece, Angelica.

Ger. Oh! as for her—that is another question. Tell me about her.

Dor. She must be suffering a great deal.

Ger. Yes, I have thought of that. I am going to see about that. I am going to find her a husband.

Dor. Well done! She certainly deserves one.

Ger. She is a charming young woman—is she not?

Dor. Yes.

Ger. Lucky the man who gets her. (*After a moment's reflection*). By the way, Dorval——

Dor. Well, my friend?

Ger. Listen.

Dor. What have you to say?

Ger. You *are* my friend?

Dor. Do you doubt it?

Ger. If you want her, I will give her to you.

Dor. Whom do you mean?

Ger. Why, my niece.

Dor. What?

Ger. You ask *what?* Are you deaf? Don't you understand? Surely I am plain enough. If you want her, I will give her to you.

Dor. Goodness gracious!

Ger. If you take her, besides her marriage portion she shall have a hundred thousand out of my pocket. Well, what do you say to that?

Dor. My dear friend, you honor me highly——

Ger. I know who and what you are, and I am certain that by this means I shall insure my niece's happiness.

Dor. But——

Ger. What?

Dor. Her brother might object.

Ger. Her brother? Her brother has nothing to do with it. It is my affair to dispose of her hand. I am master here. Come, make haste; decide at once!

Dor. What you propose is not a matter upon which a man can make up his mind in a moment. You are too impetuous.

Ger. I see no difficulty about it. If you like her, if you respect her, if she suits you, then it's all settled.

Dor. But——

Ger. But! But! What is this *but* of yours?

Dor. Do you see no disproportion in our ages—sixteen and forty-five?

Ger. None at all. You are still young, and I know Angelica; she is not a silly, frivolous creature.

Dor. Supposing, however, that she had a preference for some one else?

Ger. She has none.

Dor. Are you quite sure?

Ger. Quite sure. So let us come to an agreement at once. I will go to my notary's, I will make him draw up the settlements, and she is yours.

Dor. Gently, my dear friend, gently!

Ger. (*very angrily*). Eh? What do you say? Do you intend to worry me any longer with your dilatoriness, your beastly indifference?

Dor. So, then, you want to——

Ger. Yes, of course—give you a good, virtuous, careful

wife, with a hundred thousand as marriage portion and another hundred thousand for a wedding present. Do you consider that an offense, by any chance?

Dor. By no means. You do me an honor which I scarcely deserve.

Ger. (*in a fury*). Your confounded diffidence is just about enough to make me want to give her to the devil!

Dor. Do not be so angry. Do you really wish me to accept?

Ger. Certainly.

Dor. Very well, then; I accept——

Ger. (*delighted*). Do you?

Dor. But only provided——

Ger. Provided?

Dor. That Angelica herself consents.

Ger. Is that the only difficulty?

Dor. That is all.

Ger. Then I am satisfied. I will answer for her.

Dor. All the better, if you are sure.

Ger. Quite certain, quite sure! Embrace me, my dear nephew-in-law!

Dor. Yes, let us embrace, my dear uncle-in-law!

—"*The Beneficent Bear.*"

A Female "Solicitor of Lawsuits"

THE advocates at Venice are by regulation obliged to live in the district called Della Roba, where I accordingly engaged apartments, my mother and aunt remaining with me. I dressed up in my professional gown, the same as that worn by the patricians, pulled on an enormous wig, and anxiously waited for the day of my induction at court. This induction does not take place without ceremony. The novice must have two supporters, whom he selects from among the old advocates he knows best.

I chose two of my neighbors, both trusted friends, and we went together. I had to stand between them at the foot of the great staircase in the hall of the courts. For half an hour I was compelled to make so many bows and contortions that my back felt as if it was broken, and my wig had become as shaggy as a lion's mane. Every one who passed found some remark to make about me. Some observed that I was a boy whose face looked as if he might possibly have a little sense; others said I was a newly appointed sweeper of the courts; some kissed me, others jeered at me. At last I ascended, and sent my servant in quest of a gondola, not daring to make my appearance in the street in this costume. I ordered him to meet me in the hall of the great council, where I took a seat on a bench, and where I saw everybody pass, without being noticed by anybody.

I began to reflect on the profession I had chosen. There are generally two hundred and forty advocates on the list at Venice. Of these, ten or twelve are of the first rank, about twenty belong to the second, and all the rest are obliged to hunt for clients, the pettifogging attorneys being quite willing to play hound for the sake of a share in the quarry. I had vivid fears, as I was last on the list, and I regretted the chanceries I had left. But, on the other hand, no pursuit looked so honorable and lucrative as the advocate's. A noble Venetian, a patrician, a member of the republic, who would never condescend to be a merchant, banker, physician, or professor at a university, has no hesitation in embracing the calling of an advocate, which he follows in the courts, greeting the other advocates as his "brothers." Everything depended on good fortune, and why should I be less lucky than any one else? The attempt had to be made, and it was incumbent upon me to plunge into the chaos of the bar, where perseverance and integrity are supposed to be crowned with success.

While thus engaged in musing and building castles in the air, I observed a fair, plump woman of about thirty, with a tolerable figure, flat nose, and roguish eyes, advancing in my direction. She wore a profusion of jewelry about her neck, arms, hands, and ears, and a dress which proclaimed her one of the lower orders, though in easy circumstances. She first saluted, and then accosted me.

"Good day, sir," she said.

"Good day, madam," I replied.

The conversation being thus opened, the rest of it ran as follows:

"Will you allow me to pay you my compliments?"

"On what?"

"Why, on your admission to the courts. I could not help seeing you as you made your obeisances. Upon my word, you look handsome."

"Ah, you admire my costume? Do you think I look well in it?"

"The dress does not count at all. Signor Goldoni looks handsome in anything."

"Then you know me, madam?"

"Well, did I not see you four years ago in the land of litigation, in a long wig and a short robe?"

"Yes, you are right; I was then with an attorney."

"With Signor Indric."

"Do you know my uncle, then?"

"I? I know every soul in the place, from the doge himself down to the messengers of the courts."

"Are you married?"

"No."

"Are you a widow?"

"No."

"Have you any employment?"

"No."

"But from your appearance you seem a respectable woman."

"So I am, sir."

"Ah, then you have some private means?"

"Oh, no; none at all."

"Eh?"

"Precisely."

"But, madam, you are well dressed; how do you manage to live?"

"I am a court-girl, and make my living by the courts."

"How very curious! You belong to the courts, you say?"

"Yes, sir; my father was employed there."

"What did he do?"

"He listened at the doors, and carried good news to those expecting pardons or favorable sentences. He had good legs, so he was always first. My mother and I spent most of our time there too. She was not proud; she took commissions, and accepted money for them. I was born and brought up in those gilded halls; you see, I have gems all over me."

"Your story is quite remarkable. So you follow in the footsteps of your mother?"

"No, sir; I do something else."

"And what may that be?"

"I solicit lawsuits."

"Solicit lawsuits? I do not understand."

"I am as well known as Barabbas. It is generally understood that I am on friendly terms with all the advocates and attorneys, so that numbers of people come to me and ask me to recommend them barristers or counsel. Those who have recourse to me are not rich, as a rule, and therefore I apply to the new lawyers without briefs, who are glad of any opportunity to make their names public. Are you aware, sir, that, such as you see me, I have made the fortune of at least a dozen of the most famous advocates at this bar? You ought to feel encouraged, for, with your permission, I shall be the making of you too."

"Very well, madam, we will see. Have you any promising affair in hand at present?"

"Oh, yes, several—some of them superb. For instance, I have a widow suspected of receiving stolen goods; I have another woman who wants the validity of the fictitious date on her marriage certificate sustained; I have girls wanting marriage portions allotted to them; I have wives trying to secure a divorce; I have people of rank threatened with suit by their creditors—in fact, as you see, you have only to choose!"—*The "Memoirs."*

Carlo Frugoni

In Praise of Small People

LITTLE people, hear my song;
In your praise I'm very strong;
Great big people, go along!

In the first place, you're best made;
That's a truth can't be gainsaid,
And if it should be, who's afraid?

Beauty shows most art and grace
When she works in little space:
'Tis her most praiseworthy case.

For the force, you see, compressed,
Is forced to do its very best,
And so it's famed from east to west.

As to folk that threat the skies,
I never could, for all their size,
See whereabouts their merit lies.

Their make's all antisymmetry,
All legs and arms; and grant they be
Handsome in face, what's that, *per se?*

They look like steeples, more extensive
Than of brain-pan comprehensive.
Their clothing must be quite expensive.

And then their riding, dancing! Oh,
For my part I should like to know
How ever they could be " the go."

Now, your small man does all smugly,
Fits in every corner snugly;
And if he's ugly, he's *less* ugly.

In peril, who comes off so clean?
In a fight, who more serene?
Besides, he's very *little* seen.

Oh, littleness gives half their worth
To the rarest things on earth!
Pearls are ocean's prettiest birth.

But the big are rocks. To spy 'em
Makes the bravest that go nigh 'em
Pale, to think of passing by 'em.

Oranges are but small trees,
Yet in pots, lo! how they please;
They're the garden's *protégés*.

But your mountain pines, that throw one
At such distance, who would grow one
To adorn his window? No one.

Lastly, mastiffs. See how they,
Being big, must slink away,
Or, at best, fill kennels—eh?—

Carlo Frugoni

While your lap-dog, who refuses
To be larger than grace chooses,
All in ladies' linen snoozes.

Little people, one and all,
See if *now* your praise sings small;
See if *now* ye mind the tall!

To such reasons cut and dry,
Let their heads be ne'er so high,
What can they possibly reply?

Carlo Gozzi

Uninvited Guests

I was living in the house of my ancestors, in the Regina lane at San Cassiano. The house was very large, and I was its sole inhabitant; for my two brothers, Francesco and Almoro, had both married and settled in Friuli, leaving me this mansion as part of my inheritance. During the summer months, when people quit the city for the country, I used also to visit Friuli. I was in the habit of leaving the keys of my house with a corn merchant, my neighbor, a very honest man.

It chanced, one autumn, through one of the tricks which my evil fortune never ceased to play me, that rains and inundations kept me in Friuli longer than usual, far, indeed, into November. Snow upon the mountains, and the winds which brought fine weather, caused an intense cold. I traveled toward Venice, well enveloped in furs, traversing deep bogs, floundering through pitfalls in the road, and crossing streams in flood. At last, an hour after nightfall, I arrived, half dead with the discomforts of the journey, frozen, fatigued, and craving for sleep. I left my boat at the post-house near San Cassiano, made a porter shoulder my valise, and a servant take my hat-box under his arm. Then I set off home, wrapped up in my cape, all anxiety to crawl into a snug, warm bed.

When we reached the Regina lane we found it so crowded with people in masks and folk of both sexes, that it was quite impossible for my two attendants with their burdens to push a way to my house door.

"What the devil is the meaning of this crowd?" I asked a bystander.

"The patrician Bragadino has been made Patriarch of Venice to-day," was the man's reply. "They are illuminating, and keeping open house; bread, wine, and money are being distributed to the people for three days. That is the reason of the enormous crowd."

On reflecting that the door of my house was close to the bridge by which one passes to the square of Santa Maria, I thought that by making a turn round by the Ravano lane I might be able to get out into the square, then cross the bridge, and effect an entrance into my abode. I accomplished this long *détour* together with the bearers of my luggage, but when I reached the square I was struck dumb with astonishment at the sight of my windows thrown wide open, and my whole house ablaze with lighted candles, burning like the palace of the sun. After standing ten minutes agaze, with my mouth open in contemplation of this prodigy, I shook myself together, took heart of courage, crossed the bridge, and knocked loudly at my door. It opened, and two of the city guards presented themselves, pointing their spontoons at my breast, and crying, with fierceness written on their faces:

"There is no road this way!"

"How?" exclaimed I, still more dumfounded, and adding in a gentle voice, "Why can I not get in here?"

"No, sir," the terrible fellows answered, "there is no approach by this door. Be good enough to put on a mask, and seek entrance by the great gate which you see there on the right hand, the gate of the Bragadino Palace. As the wearer of a mask you will be permitted to pass in by that door to the feast."

"But supposing I were the master of this house, and had come home tired from a journey, half frozen, and dropping with fatigue, could I not get into my own house, and lie down in my own bed?" This I said with all possible placidity.

"Ah! the master?" replied those truculent sentinels. "Please to wait, and you will receive an answer." With these words, they slammed the door in my face.

I stared, like a man out of his senses, at my porter and my servant. The porter and the servant looked at me as though they were bewitched. At last the door opened again, and a majordomo, all laced with gold, appeared upon the threshold. With many bows and inclinations of the body, he invited me to enter. I did so, and, while passing up the staircase, asked that weighty personage what was the enchantment which had fallen on my dwelling.

"So you do not know, then!" he exclaimed. "My master, the patrician Gasparo Bragadino, foreseeing that his brother would be elected patriarch, and wanting room for the usual public festival, was desirous of uniting this house to his own by a little bridge of communication thrown across the windows. The plan was executed with your consent. It is here that a part of the feast is being celebrated, and bread and money thrown from the windows to the people. All the same, you need not fear that the room in which you sleep has not been carefully reserved, and kept scrupulously closed. Come with me, and you shall soon see for yourself."

I remained still more astonished by this news of a permission which no one had ever asked, and which I had never given. However, I did not care to bandy words with a majordomo about that. When I came into the hall I was dazzled by the huge wax candles burning, and stunned by the servants and the masks hurrying to and fro and making a mighty tumult. The noise in the kitchen attracted me to that part of the house, and I saw a huge fire, at which pots, kettles, and pipkins were boiling, while a long spit, loaded with turkeys, joints of veal, and other meats, was turning round. The majordomo meanwhile kept ceremoniously entreating me to visit my bedroom, which had been so carefully reserved and locked for me.

"Please tell me, sir," I inquired, "how late into the night this din will last?"

"To speak the truth," he answered, "it will be kept up till daybreak for three consecutive nights."

"It is a great pleasure to me," said I, "to possess anything in the world which could be of service to the Bragadino family. This circumstance has conferred an honor upon me. Pray pay my compliments to their excellencies. I shall go at once to find a lodging for the three days and three consecutive nights, being terribly in need of rest and quiet."

"Oh!" replied the majordomo, "let me entreat you to stay here, and take repose in your own house, in the room reserved for you with such great care."

"No, certainly not," I said. "I thank you for your courteous pains in my behalf. But how do you think I could sleep in the midst of all this uproar? I am unfortunately one of the lightest of sleepers."

Whereupon, bidding porter and servant follow me, I went to spend the three days and three consecutive nights in patience at an inn.—"*Useless Memoirs.*"

Giacomo Leopardi

On Reciting One's Own Compositions

JUST as Cervantes wrote a book which purged Spain of
spurious chivalry, so I, if I but possessed his genius, would
fain write one calculated to purge Italy, and indeed the
whole civilized world, of a vice which, having regard to the
humanity which in other respects characterizes the age, is
perhaps not less cruel and barbarous than any of the relics
of medieval ferocity which were lashed by the satire of
Cervantes.

I refer to the vicious practise which some writers have
of reading or reciting their compositions to their friends.
Now this offense is, indeed, of hoary antiquity; but in former
ages it was comparatively endurable, because it was comparatively rare. At the present day, however, when all men
write, and when it is most difficult to meet with a man who
is not an author, it has assumed the proportions of a social
scourge, a public calamity, and a new terror to life. Indeed,
it is no exaggeration, but the simple truth, to say that by
reason of this odious practise our acquaintances have become
objects of suspicion, and friendship itself a danger; and that
there is no time or place at which some innocent person may
not be assailed, and subjected on the spot, or be dragged
away in order to be subjected, to the torture of listening
to interminable prose compositions, or to verses by the thousand. Nor is this cruelty any longer practised under the
colorable pretext of desiring an opinion on the merits of
these compositions, as used to be the ostensible excuse for

such inflictions, but simply and solely for the pleasure it gives to the author to hear the sound of his own productions; and in order that, on the conclusion of his recitation, he may enjoy the extorted applause of his hearers.

In good sooth I think that few things are more calculated than this to exhibit the puerility of human nature, and the extreme of blindness and infatuation to which self-love is capable of conducting a man; while at the same time it is a lurid illustration of the capacity of the human mind to cheat itself with illusions. For every man knows by his own experience what an ineffable nuisance it is to have to listen to the twaddle of other people, and yet, though he sees his friends turn pale with dismay when invited to listen to *his;* though he hears them plead every imaginable pretext for escape, and perceives that they even try to flee from him and hide themselves, nevertheless, with a brazen front, and with a fell persistence like that of a famished bear, he will hunt and pursue his prey over half the town, and when he catches him he drags him to the destined scene of suffering. Then during the recitation, though he perceives, first by his yawns, then by his uneasy shiftings and contortions, and a hundred other signs, how acute are the sufferings of the unhappy listener, yet he will not desist or have mercy on him, but all the more ruthlessly continues droning on for hours, if not for entire days or evenings, until, having talked himself hoarse, and his hearer having swooned, he is at length exhausted though not sated.

Yet during this process, and throughout this torture which he inflicts on his neighbor, it is evident that he experiences a sort of superhuman delight; for we see a man, in the pursuit of this pleasure, sacrifice all other enjoyments, neglect food and repose, and forget everything else in life. And his delight arises from his firm belief that he excites the admiration of his hearer, and gives him pleasure; for if this were not so, it would serve his purpose equally well to declaim to the desert as to recite to his fellow creatures. Now, as to the pleasure conferred on the auditors—I say advisedly *auditors, not listeners*—I have just said that every one knows by experience what *that* is, and it is not concealed even from the reciter himself; and sure am I that many would prefer grievous bodily pain to such a pleasure as that. Finally, even the most beautiful and valuable compositions, when recited by their authors, are enough to bore one to death; which reminds me of the opinion of a learned friend of mine, who said that if it be true that the Empress Octavia fainted away while Vergil was reading to her the sixth canto of his *Æneid,* the probability is that her swoon was caused not by the poet's pathetic allusion to the fate of her son Marcellus, as is commonly alleged, but by sheer weariness of the reading.

Such is human nature. For this practise, so barbarous and so ridiculous, and so repugnant to common sense, springs in fact from a disease inherent in the human species, since there is not, and never has been, any nation, however polite, any condition of human society, or any age, exempt from this pest. Italians, French, English, Germans; hoary-headed men; men wise in all other respects; men of worth and genius; the most experienced in social conduct; the most finished in manners, including those most prone to note the follies of others, and to brand them with ridicule—all alike become children, and very cruel children, when they have a chance of reciting their own compositions. And just as this vice flourishes in our time, so it did in that of Horace, who declared it to be insupportable; and in that of Martial, who, being asked by an acquaintance why he did not recite

his verses, replied, " That I may escape from hearing yours."
And so it was even in the most brilliant period of ancient
Greece; since it is related that once Diogenes the cynic, finding himself present at one of these recitations, in company
with some other persons, all in a state of utter exhaustion,
and seeing at length the blank page appear at the end of
the scroll which the reciter held in his hand, he exclaimed,
" Courage, friends, I see land ! "

Nowadays, however, matters have come to such a pass
that the supply of listeners, even on compulsion, no longer
keeps pace with the demands of reciters. In these circumstances certain ingenious friends of mine have given their
serious attention to the subject, and, being persuaded that
the recitation by authors of their own compositions is one
of the most imperious needs of human nature, they have
pondered on a scheme calculated not only to satisfy it, but
also to direct its gratification, like that of other general
public needs, to the promotion of the benefit of individuals.
For this purpose they are about to open an Academy of Listening, where, at specified hours, they, or persons employed
by them, will listen to any writer desirous of reciting his
compositions. For this service there will be a fixed tariff
of charges: for listening to prose, one crown for the first
hour, two crowns for the second, four for the third, eight
crowns for the fourth hour, and so on, increasing by arithmetical progression. For listening to poetry, these charges
will be doubled. If at any time the reciter should wish to
read any particular passage a second time, as often happens,
he will be charged a florin extra for each line so repeated.
If, in the course of any reading, any of the listeners should
fall asleep, he will forfeit to the reader one-third of the fee
falling due to be paid him. To provide for the possible case

of convulsions, syncopes, or other such accesses overtaking any listener or reciter, the institution will be furnished with appropriate essences and medicines, which will be dispensed without extra charge.

In this way, the ear, which has hitherto been an unproductive organ, will become a source of direct profit to its owner, and a new path will be opened up to industry, to the increase of the public wealth.—" *Thoughts*."

Dialogue Between Fashion and Death

Fashion. Ho, Madam Death, Madam Death!

Death. Wait till your hour comes, and I'll come to you without your calling me.

Fashion. But, Madam Death——

Death. Go to Beelzebub with you! I'll come, sure enough, when you don't want me.

Fashion. Come to *me*, indeed! As if I were not immortal!

Death. Immortal, quotha! No, no—as the poet says, " A thousand years and more have passed since the times of the immortals ceased."

Fashion. Madam seems to spout her Petrarch as if she were an Italian lyric poet of the fifteenth or eighteenth century.

Death. Aye, I love the sonnets of Petrarch, for in them I find ample record of my triumphs, and they abound in mention of me. But again I say, be so good as to be off.

Fashion. Oh come! By the love you cherish for the seven cardinal sins, stop a moment and look at me!

Death. I am looking at you.

78

Giacomo Leopardi

Fashion. And do you mean to say you don't know me?

Death. You should know that my sight is bad, and that I can't use spectacles, since the English now make none that suit me; and if they did, I have no nose to stick them on.

Fashion. Why, I am Fashion, your own sister.

Death. My sister!

Fashion. Aye; don't you remember that we are both the children of Frailty?

Death. What have I to do with remembering—I, who am the sworn enemy of memory?

Fashion. But I remember the circumstance well; and I also know that both of us are alike employed continually in the destruction and change of all things here below, although you take one way of doing so, and I another.

Death. Unless you are talking to yourself, or with some person you have there inside you, I beg you will raise your voice a little and articulate your words better, for if you go on muttering to me between your teeth like that with that voice like a spider's, I'll never hear you, since, as you know, my hearing is as bad as my sight.

Fashion. Well, although it is not good manners to speak plainly, and though in France nobody speaks so as to be heard, yet, since we are sisters and need not stand on ceremony with each other, I'll speak as you wish. I say, then, that the tendency and operation common to us both is to be continually renewing the world. But whereas you have from the beginning aimed your efforts directly against the bodily constitutions and the lives of men, I am content to limit my operations to such things as their beards, their hair, their clothing, their furniture, their dwellings, and the like. Nevertheless, it is a fact that I have not failed at times to play men certain tricks not altogether unworthy to be com-

pared to your own work; as, for example, boring men's ears,
or lips, or noses, and lacerating them with the trinkets which
I place therein; or scorching their bodies with hot irons,
which I persuade them to apply to their persons by way of
improving their beauty. Then again, I sometimes squeeze
the heads of their children with ligatures and other appli-
ances, rendering it obligatory that all the inhabitants of a
country should have heads of the same shape, as I have ere
now accomplished in America and Asia. I also cripple mankind with shoes too small for their feet, and stifle their res-
piration, and make their eyes nearly start out of their heads
with tightly laced corsets, and many more follies of this kind.
In short, I contrive to persuade the more ambitious of mortals
daily to endure countless inconveniences, sometimes torture
and mutilation, aye, and even death itself, for the love they
bear toward me. I say nothing of the headaches, and colds,
and catarrhs, and fevers of all sorts, quotidian, tertian,
and quartan, which men contract through their worship of
me, inasmuch as they are willing to shiver with cold or stifle
with heat at my command, adopting the most preposterous
kinds of clothing to please me, and perpetrating a thousand
follies in my name, regardless of the consequences to themselves.

Death. By my faith, I begin to believe that you are my
sister after all. Nay, it is as sure as Death, and you have no
need to produce the birth certificate of the parish priest in
order to prove it. But standing still exhausts me, so if you've
no objection, I wish you would run on alongside of me; but
see you don't break down, for I run at a great pace. As
we run, you can tell me what it is you want of me; and even
if you would rather not keep me company, still, in consideration of your relationship to me, I promise you that when I

die I'll leave you all my effects and residuary estate, and much good may it do you.

Fashion. If we had to run a race together I don't know which of us would win, for if you run fast, I positively gallop; and as for standing still in one place, if it exhausts you, it is bane to me. So let us be off, and as we run we'll talk over our affairs.

Death. All right, then; and since you are my own mother's child, I hope it will suit you to assist me in my business.

Fashion. I've already told you that I have heretofore done so more than you would suppose. First of all, though it is my nature forever to annul and upset all other customs and usages, I have never and nowhere done anything calculated to put an end to the custom of dying; and thus, as you see, it has prevailed universally from the beginning of time till now.

Death. A precious marvel, forsooth, that you have abstained from doing that which it was not in your power to do!

Fashion. Not in my power, quotha! It is very evident that you have no idea of the power of Fashion.

Death. Well, well, it'll be time enough to discuss this point when the custom of dying comes to an end. But in the meantime I want you, as a good and affectionate sister, to help me to prevent such a result, and to attain its very opposite, even more effectually and more expeditiously than I have yet done.—*"Dialogues."*

Dialogue Between the Earth and the Moon

Earth. My dear Moon, I know you can talk, and answer questions, since you are a person, as I have often heard from the poets; besides which, our children say you have really got a mouth and nose and eyes, just like any one of themselves, and that they can see this with their own eyes, which at their time of life indeed are pretty sharp. As for me, I doubt not you know that I, too, am no less a person; so much so, indeed, that when I was younger I had plenty of children of my own; and so you won't be surprised to hear me talk.

Well, then, my sweet Moon, though I have been so close to you for so many ages that I can't remember their number, I have never yet addressed a word to you till now, because my own affairs have hitherto so occupied me that I have never before found time for a chat. But now that my business is so reduced that it can take care of itself, I don't know what to do with myself, and am fairly bursting with boredom. Therefore I propose in future to talk to you often, and to take much interest in your affairs—that is to say, provided I shall not thereby be troublesome to you.

Moon. Have no anxiety on that score. I would I were as certain that fortune would insure me against all other inconveniences, as I am certain that *you* will not cause me any. If you want to talk to me, talk away at your pleasure, for, although I am a lover of silence, as I think you know, yet, to oblige you, I am willing to listen to you, and even to answer your questions.

Earth. Well, then, to begin. Do you hear the delicious

harmony which the heavenly bodies produce by their revolutions?

Moon. To tell you the truth, I hear nothing.

Earth. Well, for the matter of that, no more do I, unless it be the roar of the wind as it rushes from my poles to the equator, or from the equator to the poles, and there's not much music in that. But Pythagoras asserts that the celestial spheres create a certain wonderfully sweet sound, and that you yourself contribute to it, and actually form the eighth chord of the universal lyre; but he adds that I am deafened by the sound of it, and therefore do not hear it.

Moon. Then, of a surety, I, too, must be deafened by it, for, as I said just now, I do not hear it; and I do not feel like being a chord.

Earth. Well, let us change the subject. Tell me, are you really inhabited, as has been alleged and sworn to by a thousand philosophers, ancient and modern, from Orpheus down to De Lalande? As for me, no matter how I try to stretch these horns of mine which men call mountain peaks, and from which I stare at you, just like a snail with extended horns, yet I never can make out a single inhabitant on you; though I have heard that one David Fabricius, whose eyesight was sharper even than that of Lynceus, once saw some of them spreading their linen out in the sun to dry.

Moon. As to your horns, as you call them, I know nothing about them; but the fact is, I *am* inhabited.

Earth. Aye, and what color are your men?

Moon. Men! What men?

Earth. Those who live on you, of course. Do not you say you are inhabited?

Moon. Well, so I am; but what of that?

Earth. Well, I presume not *all* your inhabitants are brutes?

Moon. Neither brutes nor men. Indeed, for the matter of that, I do not even know what sorts of creatures brutes or men may be; and I may as well tell you that I have not understood a syllable of these things you have just been saying to me, about these men, I presume.

Earth. Then what sort of creatures are these inhabitants of yours?

Moon. They are of many and various sorts, all of them unknown to you, as yours are to me.

Earth. This strikes me as so strange that had I not heard it from your own lips I should never have believed it possible. Were you ever conquered by any of your inhabitants?

Moon. Not to my knowledge. Conquered? How do you mean, and why?

Earth. Well, for ambition or cupidity, and by means of political arts or force of arms.

Moon. I do not know what you mean by arms, or ambition, or political arts. In fact, I do not know what you are talking about.

Earth. Nay, surely, if you do not know what arms are, you assuredly know what war is, for, not long ago, a certain philosopher down here, by means of certain instruments called telescopes, which enable people to see a great distance, plainly saw up there on you a first-class fortress with tall bastions—a thing which proves that your people are accustomed at least to sieges and mural combats.

Moon. Pardon me, Madam Earth, if I reply to you a trifle more freely than is perhaps becoming in one who, like me, is only your vassal and handmaiden. But I really must say you appear to me something more than overvain in supposing that all things in all parts of creation must be similar to what prevails in your limits, as if Nature had no other idea except to copy *you* exactly in all her operations. When I tell you that I am inhabited, straightway you must jump to the conclusion that my inhabitants must be men. Then, when I tell you that they are not so, and when you seem to realize that they may possibly be creatures of some other species, you immediately assume that they must have the same properties and must live under the same conditions as your people, and begin to tell me about telescopes and philosophers and what not. But if these telescopes do not enable you to examine other things more accurately than it seems they do in my case, then I suspect their accuracy is on a par with that of the children down there on you, who, as you have just said, discover in me a mouth and nose and eyes, which I have no knowledge of possessing.

Earth. I suppose you will tell me next that it is not true that your provinces are provided with fine broad roads, or that you are cultivated, although these things can be plainly seen from Germany with the help of a telescope.

Moon. If I am cultivated, I am not conscious of the fact; and as to the alleged roads on my surface, they are invisible to me.

Earth. My dear Moon, I would have you to know that I am rather uneducated and something dull in understanding, and so it is no wonder if men easily impose on me. But, nevertheless, I am in a position to tell you that though, as you say, your own inhabitants have never evinced a desire to conquer you, still you have not always been quite free from dangers of this kind; since at various times various people down here have cherished schemes of conquering you themselves, and have even proceeded far in their preparations to that end. And truly they might have succeeded in their attempts, were it not that although they ascended to the highest points on my surface, and stood on their tiptoes, and stretched out their arms as far as ever they could, they somehow never managed to reach you. Besides this, for some years past I have observed that my people have been carefully surveying every part of you, and drawing up maps of your various countries. They have also measured the heights of your mountains, and they know the names of them all. Well, for the good-will I bear you, I have thought it only right to tell you of these things, in order that you may be prepared for all possible contingencies.

But now to come to some other matters which I want to ask you. How ever do you stand the incessant baying of our dogs at you? What is your opinion of those people who show you to their friends in a well? Are you feminine or masculine? For in former times opinions were much divided on this point. Is it a fact that the Arcadians existed before you were made? Is it true that the women on you, or whatever your female inhabitants ought to be called, are oviparous, and that an egg of one of them actually fell down here once upon a time, I know not when? Is it the case that you are perforated just like the bead of a rosary, as is maintained by a modern philosopher; or that you are made of green cheese, as certain Englishmen affirm? Are we to believe that one day, or it may have been one night, Mohammed sliced you in two through the middle like a watermelon, and that a good large piece of you slipped up his sleeve? And, finally, why do you like to hang on the tops of minarets; and what are your views as to the feast of Bairam?

Moon. Perhaps you will be good enough to ask me a few

more questions, for while you run on like this I have no need to answer you, and can comfortably maintain my wonted silence. If it pleases you to indulge in chatter like this, and can find nothing more sensible to talk about, then, instead of addressing yourself to me, who do not know what you mean, I would recommend you to get your inhabitants to manufacture for you a brand-new satellite which shall revolve round you, and which shall be composed and peopled after your own notions. Apparently you can talk of nothing but men and dogs and other things of which I know no more than I do of that stupendous sun round which it is said our own sun rotates.

Earth. I confess that the more I resolve, in my conversation with you, to avoid topics specially connected with myself, the less do I succeed in doing so. But I shall be still more careful in future. So now, is it you who amuse yourself by alternately raising and depressing the water in my oceans?

Moon. Possibly it may be so, but whether I do that, or produce any other effects on you, I am no more conscious of the fact than you probably are of the many effects which you produce on me; and you may imagine that they must exceed those of me on you in proportion as you excel me in size and power.

Earth. As to any effects that I may produce on you I am not aware of any except that from time to time I intercept from you the light of the sun, and your own from myself; and also that while it is night with you, I shine very brightly on you, as indeed I myself occasionally perceive. But I was nearly forgetting a point which interests me above all others. I should like to know if Ariosto is right where he declares that all the properties which men are continually losing, such as youth, beauty, health, and the like, as well as all the efforts which they expend in the pursuit of earthly renown, in the education of their children, and in the promotion of so-called useful objects—I say, I should like to know if it is true that all these things evaporate in your direction, and are eventually piled up in you as in a lumber-room, so that all human things are to be found there, except, indeed, folly, which never departs from men. If this be so, I reckon that by this time you must be pretty well crammed, and must have very little spare room left; the more so, seeing that of late men have been parting with an unusual number of things, such as patriotism, virtue, magnanimity, and rectitude; and this not only partially or exceptionally, as used to be the case, but universally and totally. At all events, if these things have not flown away to you, I do not know where else they can be. Well, I would propose that we enter into a convention, by the terms of which you shall agree to return these things to me, either at once or by degrees. I judge it likely that you would be glad to be rid of them, especially of common sense, which, I hear, takes up a great deal of space on your globe. On the other hand, I for my part will cause my inhabitants to pay you a good round sum annually for this accommodation.

Moon. Still harping on those blessed men! For all you have said as to folly never leaving your confines, you are like to drive *me* mad, and rob me of my own share of common sense in your search for that of men, as to which I have no sort of idea where it is, or whether it still exists in any corner of the universe. The only thing I do know about it is that it is not to be found up here—no, nor any of the other things you ask me for.

Earth. Well, then, at least tell me if your inhabitants are acquainted with vices, misdeeds, misfortunes, pain, old age, and, in a word, all ills. I presume you know the meaning of these names.

Moon. Oh, I know them well; and not only the names, but the things which they mean. Too well do I know them, for I am filled quite full with them, instead of with the other things you mentioned just now.

Earth. Which most abound among your inhabitants— virtues or vices?

Moon. Vices, by a very long way indeed.

Earth. And, with you, which generally predominates— good or evil?

Moon. Evil, beyond all comparison.

Earth. And, generally speaking, are your inhabitants happy or unhappy?

Moon. So unhappy that I would not change places with the most fortunate of them.

Earth. It is just the same down here; so much so that it is a marvel to me that you, who differ so totally from me in other respects, should resemble me exactly in this.

Moon. Nay, I resemble you also in form, in rotatory movement, and in being illumined by the sun; and the resemblance you marvel at is no more wonderful than our resemblance in these other particulars, seeing that evil is a condition as common to all the planets of the universe— or, at all events, of our solar system—as is rotundity and the other points just noted by me. Indeed, I will venture to say that if you could raise your voice so as to be heard by Uranus or Saturn, or any other planet of our system, and were to ask it whether unhappiness existed there, or whether good or evil most prevailed within its limits, any one of them would give you the same answer that I have done. This I am prepared to assert, because I put these very questions to Venus and to Mercury, which two planets from time to time approach more closely to me than I do to you; and I have also asked the same thing from one or two comets which happened to pass near me, and all alike replied in the same terms. Nay, I am quite confident that the sun himself, and all the fixed stars, would say the same.

Earth. Well, for all you say, I hope for the best, and especially at this time, since men assure me of great happiness in the near future.

Moon. Hope away as much as you please. I promise you that you will have to be content with hoping forever.

Earth. Hush! Observe—do you see what's happening? The men and animals are beginning to stir. You know that down here it is night, and they were all sleeping; but, alarmed by our talking in this way, they are all awaking in mortal terror.

Moon. But with me, as you see, it is day.

Earth. Well, well, I do not wish to frighten my creatures and disturb their sleep, which, poor things, is the greatest consolation they possess. So we'll leave off now, and resume our conversation another time. So good day to you.

Moon. Good night.—" *Dialogues.*"

The Academy of Syllographs

THE Academy of Syllographs, ever mindful of the primary aim of its constitution, and having always at heart the promotion of the public good, has come to the conclusion that it could not more effectually conduce to this end than by aiding in the development of the distinguishing tendencies of what an illustrious poet has characterized as the happy age in which we live.

For this reason it has diligently diagnosed the genius of the present time, and after prolonged and searching investigation it has arrived at the conviction that the present age ought to be characterized as preeminently the age of machines. And this not only because the men of to-day live and move more mechanically than did those of any former period, but also by reason of the infinite number of mechanical contrivances continually being invented, and daily being applied to so many various purposes, that nowadays it may almost be said that human affairs and all the operations of life are governed and regulated not by men at all, but by machines.

This feature of the age is hailed by the Academy with peculiar satisfaction, not only in view of the manifest general convenience which flows from it, but also for two special reasons of a most important character, though not generally recognized by society. In the first place, the Academy feels confident that in course of time the agency of mechanism may be so extended as to embrace not only the material but the moral world; and that, just as mechanical inventions now protect us from lightning and other atmospherical disturbances, so, in time, some sort of apparatus may be invented calculated to shield us from envy, calumny, perfidy, and fraud; some species of moral lightning-conductors, so to speak, which may protect us from the effects of egotism, from the dominion of mediocrity, from the arrogance of bloated imbecility, from the ribaldry of the base, from the cynical pessimism of pedants, from the indifferentism engendered by overculture, and from numerous other such like inconveniences, which of late have become as difficult to ward off as formerly were the lightnings and storms of the physical world.

The next consideration just referred to is this, and it is one of paramount importance. It is well known that philosophers have come to despair of remedying the manifold defects of humanity, and are convinced that it would be more difficult to amend these than it would be to recast things on an entirely fresh basis, and to substitute an entirely fresh agency as the motive power of life. The Academy of Syllographs, concurring in this opinion, hold that it would be in the highest degree expedient that men should retire as far as possible from the conduct of the business of the world, and should gradually give place to mechanical agency for the direction of human affairs. Accordingly, resolved to contribute as far as lies in its power to this consummation, it has determined to offer three prizes, to be awarded to the persons who shall invent the best examples of the three machines now to be described.

The scope and object of the first of these automata shall be to represent the person and discharge the functions of a friend who shall not calumniate or jeer at his absent associate; who shall not fail to take his part when he hears him censured or ridiculed; who shall not prefer a reputation for wit, and the applause of men, to his duty to friendship; who shall never, from love of gossip or mere ostentation of superior knowledge, divulge a secret committed to his keeping; who shall not abuse the intimacy or confidence of his fellow in order to supplant or surpass him; who shall harbor no envy against his friend; who shall guard his interests and help to repair his losses, and shall be prompt to answer his call, and minister to his needs more substantially than by empty professions.

In the construction of this piece of mechanism it will be well to study, among other things, the treatise on friendship by Cicero, as well as that of Madame de Lambert. The Academy is of opinion that the manufacture of such a machine ought not to prove impracticable or even particularly difficult, for, besides the automata of Regiomontanus and Vaucanson, there was at one time exhibited in London a mechanical figure which drew portraits, and wrote to dictation; while there have been more than one example of such machines capable of playing at chess. Now, in the opinion of many philosophers human life is but a game; nay, some hold that it is more shallow and more frivolous than many other games, and that the principles of chess, for example, are more in accordance with reason, and that its various moves are more governed by wisdom, than are the actions of mankind; while we have it on the authority of Pindar that human action is no more substantial than the shadow of a dream; and this being so, the intelligence of an automaton ought to prove quite equal to the discharge of the functions which have just been described.

As to the power of speech, it seems unreasonable to doubt that men should have the power of communicating it to machines constructed by themselves, seeing that this may be said to have been established by sundry precedents, such, for example, as in the case of the statue of Memnon, and of the human head manufactured by Albertus Magnus, which actually became so loquacious that Saint Thomas Aquinas, losing all patience with it, smashed it to pieces. Then, too, there was the instance of the parrot Ver-Vert, though it was a living creature; but if it could be taught to converse reasonably, how much more may it be supposed that a machine devised by the mind of man, and constructed by his hands, should do as much; while it would have this advantage that it might be made less garrulous than this parrot, or the head of Albertus, and therefore it need not irritate its acquaintances and provoke them to smash it.

The inventor of the best example of such a machine shall be decorated with a gold medallion of four hundred sequins in weight, bearing on its face the images of Pylades and Orestes, and on the reverse the name of the successful competitor, surrounded by the legend, First Realizer of the Fables of Antiquity.

The second machine called for by the Academy is to be an artificial steam man, so constructed and regulated as to perform virtuous and magnanimous actions. The Academy is of opinion that in the absence of all other adequate motive power to that end, the properties of steam might prove effective to inspire an automaton, and direct it to the attainment of virtue and true glory. The inventor who shall undertake the construction of such a machine should study the poets and the writers of romance, who will best guide him as to the qualities and functions most essential to such a piece of mechanism. The prize shall be a gold medal weighing four hundred and fifty sequins, bearing on its obverse a figure symbolical of the golden age, and on its reverse the name of the inventor.

The third automaton should be so constituted as to perform the duties of woman such as she was conceived by the Count Baldassar Castiglione, and described by him in his treatise entitled *The Courtier,* as well as by other writers in other works on the subject, which will be readily found, and which, as well as that of the count, will have to be carefully consulted and followed. The construction of a machine of this nature, too, ought not to appear impossible to the inventors of our time, when they reflect on the fact that in the most ancient times, and times destitute of science, Pygmalion was able to fabricate for himself, with his own hands, a wife of such rare gifts that she has never since been equaled down to the present day. The successful inventor of this machine shall be rewarded with a gold medal weighing five hundred sequins, bearing on one face the figure of the Arabian Phenix of Metastasio, couched on a tree of a European species, while its other side will bear the name of the inventor, with the title, INVENTOR OF FAITHFUL WOMEN AND OF CONJUGAL HAPPINESS.

Finally, the Academy has resolved that the funds necessary to defray the expenses incidental to this competition shall be supplemented by all that was found in the purse of Diogenes, its first secretary, together with one of the three golden asses which were the property of three of its former members—namely, Apuleius, Firenzuola, and Machiavelli, but which came into the possession of the Academy by the last wills and testaments of the aforementioned, as duly recorded in its minutes.—"*Essays.*"

The Origin of Laughter

THE song of birds affords keen delight not to man alone, but to all other animals. I believe this arises not from the mere sweetness and variety of its harmony, great as these properties unquestionably are, but mainly from that suggestion of gladness naturally inherent in all song, and more especially in that of birds. It is, in a word, the laughter of these creatures which convulses them when they are happy.

From this circumstance it may almost be said that birds share with man the power and privilege of laughing, which none of the other animals possess. Hence, some have held that as man has been defined as an intellectual and reasoning animal, he might equally well have been distinguished as a laughing one, seeing that the power to laugh is as peculiar to man as is the gift of reason. But is it not a strange thing that while man is the most afflicted of all animals, he is the only one which possesses the power to laugh, a gift withheld from all other creatures on earth? Strange, too, is the use we sometimes make of this faculty, since even in the most acute calamities, in the profoundest distress, when life itself is odious, when the vanity of all earthly things is most apparent, when joy is impossible and hope is dead, men are seen to laugh! Nay, the more they realize the vanity of all earthly joys and the reality of human misery, and the more hopeless and indisposed to merriment they are, the more do we find some men prone to laughter! Indeed, the very nature of laughter, and its governing principles and motives, are so inexplicable that sometimes it may best be described as a sort of transient madness, a temporary delirium of the soul. For, in truth, men, being never truly satisfied or really delighted by anything, can never have a just and reasonable cause for laughter. In fact, it would be curious to inquire how and under what circumstances man first became conscious of his possession of this faculty, and first actually employed it. For it is certain that in his primitive and savage state he is generally grave in his demeanor, and indeed apparently melancholy in his mood, as are the lower animals.

For this reason, not only am I convinced that laughter made its appearance in the world subsequently to tears—a point, indeed, on which there can be little doubt—but also that a long period must have elapsed before it may be said to have been even discovered. During this period it may be assumed, as, indeed, is expressly stated by Vergil, that not even the mother smiled upon her babe, nor did the babe recognize its mother with a smile. And if at the present time, at least in civilized societies, man begins to laugh soon after his birth, I am of opinion that this is mainly the effect of example and imitation, and that children laugh because they see others do so.

For my part, I am disposed to think that laughter had its origin in intoxication, itself a condition peculiar to the human race. And we know that intoxication prevailed among men long before they had attained to civilization; as is proved by the fact that the rudest peoples are acquainted with intoxicants of one kind or another, and use them with avidity. Nor is this to be wondered at, for men are, of all animals, the most exposed to unhappiness, and therefore they alone are impelled to seek consolation in this soothing mental alienation, which, inducing forgetfulness of self, amounts to a temporary intermission of life itself, during which the sense of suffering is diminished, or actually suspended for a time. And, as touching laughter in this connection, it is a familiar fact that savages, who in their sober moments are usually serious and sad, when intoxicated laugh immoderately, and even chatter and sing, contrary to their usual custom. However, I propose to treat this question more fully in a history of laughter, which I contemplate composing, and in which, after investigating its origin, I shall follow up its development and vicissitudes down to the present time, when, as we see, it flourishes exuberantly, and occupies in the economy of civilized life a position almost equal to that formerly filled by virtue, justice, honor, and the like, wielding an influence scarcely inferior to that exercised by those principles.

—*"The Praise of Birds," in the "Essays."*

Alberto Nota

The Purchase of a Greek Manuscript

GERONZIO; FAUSTINA, *his Niece;* MENICA, *his Housekeeper.*

Ger. I cannot imagine, niece, how that young man, who knows nothing in the world, has made such a good impression on you. I am sure he has not a single book in his house beyond the almanac. Now, what would you do in such a house as that? Yes, what would there be to do?

Faus. I should be the mother of a family. When a woman knows how to keep her accounts and manage her household economically, there is no necessity for her to spend much time in reading or studying. My poor mother used to say—and you remember it too—that women who are bluestockings drive their husbands mad and turn their houses upside down.

Ger. Very well. But are you obliged to marry? Can you not live quietly with your uncle, and continue improving your mind more and more?

Men. A fine proposition!

Faus. No, that is not at all to my taste.

Ger. You would by degrees reject all base, material ideas——

Men. And in the meantime live on air——

Ger. And would taste the supreme joys of an intellectual life——

Men. The kitchen has been empty for three years——

Ger. Among the venerable fathers of Greek and Roman literature, and among rare manuscripts and prints——

Men. And, instead of dishes and kettles, full of old papers and dusty books——

Ger. Which are the proper possessions for all well-educated people.

Men. But there's very little to eat.

Ger. A frugal existence keeps one healthy and strong, the passions are not inflamed, the mind is clear, the understanding is free, the——

Men. And this morning it is freer than ever, because we have had no breakfast yet.

Ger. Faustina, I hope you paid particular attention to that Dutch bookseller with whom we walked along the esplanade yesterday and the day before, and who was so much interested in you.

Faus. What do you mean?

Ger. He has a magnificent collection, and has come to Italy to increase it. As you insist on marrying, there is a splendid match for you.

Faus. It is no use; you know what my views are on that subject.

Ger. He is coming to see me to-day——

Men. Some money, sir, if you please——

Ger. And how astonished he will be to find that volume of Arabic poetry by Sathian-Mum-Gabner, which was carried off from the mosque at Mecca——

Men. But, master——

Ger. And the two valuable documents in Coptic——

Men. I beg of you——

Ger. And the three papyri from Herculaneum, and those volumes in the Basque language, and then those others I am expecting from Naples. But I must go and put that Petrarch away.

. . . .

GERONZIO, FAUSTINA, MENICA, and ERGILIO.

Erg. Sir, I did not expect to trouble you again——

Ger. An honor, I assure you. Make yourself at home.

Erg. I am in rather a hurry. This morning I sold you that beautiful, that superb edition of Petrarch.

Ger. Well? Do you regret the bargain?

Erg. No, but——

Ger. Ah, then you have more books to dispose of!

Men. Master, please remember——

Faus. Uncle, please consider——

Ger. Oh, hush, both of you, and go away!

Erg. I have a number of Elzevirs, Bodonianis, Barbous, Didots.

Ger. No, thank you, for the present.

Men. (*to* FAUSTINA). Thank the Lord!

Ger. But if you had some fine old codex——

Erg. I just came to show you a very rare Greek manuscript on Egyptian papyrus.

Ger. On Egyptian papyrus!

Erg. Yes, sir, on Egyptian papyrus. (*Takes from his pocket a volume, which* GERONZIO *lays on a table and begins to examine minutely.*) You will also find some scholarly notes which will interest you. (*Signs to* FAUSTINA *and* MENICA *that he has a letter.*)

Ger. Ah, ah, very fine, very handsome! Patience, now, and I shall soon be able to tell you something about this.

Faus. (*to* MENICA). Did you see?

Men. (*to* FAUSTINA). Yes, a letter, it seems,

101

Ger. So your father was a learned bibliophile?

Erg. He was a great lover of books; he had over four thousand volumes.

Ger. But I have ten thousand. And are they really autograph notes?

Erg. I don't understand.

Ger. (*aside*). Poor fellow!—I mean, are they handwritten?

Erg. Oh, I understand! Yes, sir, all in my father's own handwriting! But pray observe the beauty of that papyrus; it is entirely unique.

Ger. Yes, quite unique.

Erg. So my father used to say.

Ger. Yes, there is no other specimen like it. Let us all look at it together. Come here, niece, and you, Menica, come too.

Erg. It cost my father fifty crowns.

Ger. (*to the women*). Don't touch! Don't touch! How beautiful! And in Greek characters! Fancy, niece! Fancy, Menica! Oh, how beautiful!

Faus. How magnificent!

Men. How splendid!

> (MENICA *has meanwhile secretly got the letter from* ERGILIO, *and hands it to* FAUSTINA, *who slips aside to read it.*)

Ger. But, my dear sir, fifty crowns! And in such times as these! (*Aside.*) I should not like him to show it to the Dutch bookseller.

Erg. I will be reasonable. My father bought it to gratify a hobby, and I am selling it from necessity. Examine the book, and we may come to terms.

Ger. What does it treat of?

Erg. What! you do not know Greek?

Ger. No, not I!

Erg. And you buy books in Greek?

Ger. I have books in Greek, in Hebrew, in Arabic, in German, in Chinese, and even in Sanskrit. You are surprised? Not every one who owns a large library can read the volumes he has bought.

Erg. My father knew Greek very well. He told me this book contained the famous dialogues between Socrates, his familiar demon, and Xantippe, the philosopher's wife.

Ger. They must be delightful!

Erg. Yes; imagine a philosopher, a woman, and a demon, all together.

Ger. What exquisite things they must have said!

Erg. You will find in the notes that, after the philosopher's death, the women of Athens rushed to his house to seize upon these writings, probably because they did not wish such savory comments on the state of marital bliss to be published.

Ger. And how was the papyrus saved?

Erg. Through a miracle of the gods. It was taken to Rome in the reign of Augustus, and placed in the renowned library of the Palatine Apollo.

Ger. What fine things must be there!

Erg. And my father acquired it from a bookseller in Germany.

Ger. Your father had more intellect than you, if I am not mistaken.

Erg. But less cheerfulness and happiness of disposition.

Ger. Have you not studied at all?

Erg. Music—nothing else. I play the piano, the violin, the violoncello; I sing tenor, compose little songs——

Ger. Let me consult my catalogues. (*While doing so, mutters to himself.*) He is in want of money, and he does not know the value of these precious articles. So much the better for me.—I do not find the title of this work in my index.

Erg. Then you don't care to buy it?

Men. (*aside*). I hope he won't.

Ger. If you could only leave it with me until to-morrow——

Erg. Not for an hour. I would rather make a sacrifice.

Ger. Well—er—about how much?

Erg. Oh, I am in a hurry! I will let you have it—yes, I will let you have it for—fifteen crowns.

Ger. If you could take ten——

Men. (*aside*). We are done for.

Erg. Ten is very little.

Ger. Well, here are ten crowns. You will not get a penny more out of me.

Erg. Let me see. Very well—take it, then, and think yourself lucky to get a philosopher, a woman, and a demon, all together, for ten crowns.—"*The Bibliomaniac.*"

Alessandro Manzoni

Don Abbondio's Encounter with the Outlaws

TOWARD evening, on November 7, 1628, the vicar, Don
Abbondio, was returning slowly toward his home. He was
quietly repeating his prayers, in the pauses of which he
held his closed breviary in his hand behind his back; and
as he went, with his foot he listlessly kicked against the wall
the stones that happened to impede his path, at the same
time giving admittance to the idle thoughts that tempted
the spirit, while the lips of the worthy man were mechanically performing their function. Then, raising his head and
gazing idly around him, he fixed his eyes upon a mountain
summit, where the rays of the setting sun, breaking through
the openings of an opposite ridge, illumined its projecting
masses, which appeared like large and variously shaped spots
of purple light. He then opened his breviary anew and recited another portion at an angle of the lane, after which
angle the road continued straight for perhaps seventy paces,
and then split like the letter Y into two narrow paths; the
right-hand branch ascended toward the mountain, and led
to the parsonage; that on the left descended the valley toward
a torrent, and on this side the wall rose out to the height of
about two feet. The inner walls of the two narrow paths,
instead of meeting at the angle, ended at a little chapel, upon
which were depicted certain long, sinuous, pointed shapes,
which, in the intention of the artist, and to the eyes of the
neighboring inhabitants, represented flames, and amid these
flames certain other forms, not to be described, that were

meant for souls in purgatory—souls and flames of a brick
color, upon a ground of blackish gray, with here and there
a bare spot of plaster. The priest, having turned the corner, directed, as was his wont, a look toward the little chapel,
and there beheld what he little expected, and would not have
desired to see.

At the confluence, if we may so call it, of the two narrow
lanes, there were two men, one of them sitting astride the
low wall, his companion leaning against it, with his arms
folded on his breast. The dress, the bearing, and what the
minister could distinguish of the countenance of these men,
left no doubt as to their profession. They wore upon their
heads a cap of green network, which, falling on the left
shoulder, ended in a large tassel, from under which appeared
upon the forehead an enormous lock of hair. Their mus-
taches were long, and curled at the extremities; the margin
of their doublets confined by a belt of polished leather, from
which were suspended, by hooks, two pistols; a little powder-
horn hung like a locket on the breast; on the right-hand side
of the wide and ample breeches was a pocket, out of which
projected the handle of a knife, and on the other side they
bore a long sword, of which the great hollow hilt was formed
of bright plates of brass, combined into a cipher.

It appeared evident to Don Abbondio that the two men
above-mentioned were waiting for some one, and he was
alarmed at the conviction that it was for himself; for on
his appearance they exchanged a look, as if to say, " 'Tis
he." Rising from the wall, they both advanced to meet him.
He held his breviary open before him, as though he were
employed in reading it, but, nevertheless, cast a glance up-
ward in order to espy their movements. Seeing that they
came directly toward him, he was beset by a thousand differ-

ent thoughts. He considered, in haste, whether between the bravos and himself there were any outlet from the road, and he remembered there was none. He took a rapid survey of his conduct, to discover if he had given offense to any powerful or revengeful man; but in this matter he was somewhat reassured by the consoling testimony of his conscience. The bravos drew near, and kept their eyes upon him. He raised his hand to his collar, as if adjusting it, and at the same time turned his head round, to see if any one were coming. He could discover no one. He cast a glance across the low stone wall upon the fields. No one! Another on the road that lay before him. No one except the bravos!

What was to be done? Flight was impossible. Unable to avoid the danger, he hastened to encounter it, and to put an end to the torments of uncertainty. He quickened his pace, recited a few lines in a louder tone, did his utmost to assume a composed and cheerful countenance, and finding himself in front of the two gallants, stopped short.

"Reverend sir," said one of them, fixing his eyes upon him.

"Your pleasure, sir," suddenly raising his eyes from his book, which he continued to hold open before him.

"You intend," pursued the other, with the threatening and angry mien of one who has detected an inferior in an attempt to commit some villainy, "you intend to-morrow to unite in marriage Renzo Tramaglino and Lucia Mondella."

"That is," said Don Abbondio with a faltering voice, "that is to say—you gentlemen, being men of the world, are very well aware how these things are managed: the poor vicar neither meddles nor makes; they settle their affairs among themselves, and then—then they come to us, as if to redeem a pledge; and we—we are the servants of the public."

"Mark, now," said the bravo in a low voice, but in a tone of command, "this marriage is not to take place, neither to-morrow, nor at any other time."

"But, my good sirs," replied Don Abbondio, with the mild and gentle tone of one who would persuade an impatient lis-tener—"but, my good sirs, deign to put yourselves in my place. If the thing depended on myself—you see plainly that it does not in the least concern——"

"Hold, there!" said the bravo, interrupting him. "This matter is not to be settled by prating. We neither know nor care to know any more about it. A man once warned —you understand us."

"But, fair sirs, you are too just, too reasonable——"

"But," interrupted the other comrade, who had not before spoken—"but this marriage is not to be performed, or" (with an oath) "he who performs it will not repent of it, because he'll not have time" (with another oath).

"Hush, hush," resumed the first orator, "the reverend gentleman knows the world, and we have no wish to harm him if he conducts himself with judgment. Sir, the most illustrious Lord Don Roderigo, our patron, offers you his kind regards."

As in the height of a midnight storm a vivid flash casts a momentary dazzling glare around and renders every object more fearful, so did this name increase the terror of Don Abbondio. As if by instinct, he bowed his head submissively, and said:

"If it could only be suggested to me."

"Oh! suggested to *you*, who understand Latin!" exclaimed the bravo, laughing. "It is for you to manage the matter.

But, above all, be careful not to say a word concerning the hint that has been given you for your good; for if you do— ahem!—you understand—the consequences would be the same as if you performed the marriage ceremony. But say, what answer are we to carry in your name to our illustrious Lord Don Roderigo?"

"My respects——"

"Speak more clearly, your reverence."

"That I am disposed, ever disposed, to obedience." And as he spoke the words he was not very certain himself whether he gave a promise, or only uttered an ordinary compliment. The bravos took or appeared to take them in the more serious sense.

"'Tis well. Good night, your reverence," said one of them as he retired, together with his companion. Don Abbondio, who a few minutes before would have given one of his eyes to avoid the ruffians, was now desirous to prolong the conversation.

"Gentlemen—" he began, as he shut his book. Without again noticing him, however, they passed on, singing a loose song, of which we will not transcribe the words. Poor Don Abbondio remained for a moment as if spellbound, and then with heavy and lagging steps took the path which led toward his home. . . .

Having, amid the tumult of his thoughts, reached the entrance of his house, which stood at the end of the little glebe, he unlocked the door, entered, and carefully secured it within. Anxious to find himself in society that he could trust, he called aloud, "Perpetua! Perpetua!" advancing toward the little parlor where she was doubtless employed in preparing the table for his supper. Perpetua was, as the reader must learn, the housekeeper of Don Abbondio, an affectionate and faithful domestic, who knew how to obey or command, as occasion served, to bear the grumbling and whims of her master at times, and at others to make him bear with hers. These were becoming every day more frequent; she had passed the age of forty in the single state; the consequence, she said, of having refused all the offers that had been made her, her female friends asserting that she had never found any one willing to take her.

"Coming," said Perpetua, as she set in its usual place on the little table the flask of Don Abbondio's favorite wine, and moved slowly toward the parlor door. Before she reached it he entered, with steps so disordered, looks so clouded, and a countenance so changed, that an eye less practised than that of Perpetua could have discovered at a glance that something unusual had befallen him.

"Mercy on me! What is it ails my master?"

"Nothing, nothing," said Don Abbondio, as he sank upon his easy chair.

"How, nothing! Would you have me believe that, looking as you do? Some dreadful accident has happened."

"Oh, for the love of Heaven! When I say nothing, it is either nothing, or something I must not tell."

"That you cannot tell, not even to me? Who will take care of your health? Who will give you advice?"

"Oh! peace, peace! Do not make matters worse. Give me a glass of my wine."

"And you will still pretend to me that nothing is the matter?" said Perpetua, filling the glass, but retaining it in her hand, as if unwilling to present it except as the reward of confidence.

"Give it to me," said Don Abbondio, taking the glass with an unsteady hand and hastily swallowing its contents.

"Would you oblige me, then, by going about asking here and there what it is that has happened to my master?" said Perpetua, standing upright before him, with her hands on her sides, and looking him steadfastly in the face, as if to extract the secret from his eyes.

"For the love of Heaven, do not worry me, do not kill me with your pother! This is a matter that concerns—concerns my life."

"Your life!"

"My life."

"You know well that, when you have frankly confided in me, I have never——"

"Yes, forsooth, as when——"

Perpetua was sensible she had touched a false string; wherefore, changing suddenly her note, "My dear master," said she, in a moving tone of voice, "I have always had a dutiful regard for you, and if I now wish to know this affair, it is from zeal, and a desire to assist you, to give you advice, to relieve your mind."

The truth is, that Don Abbondio's desire to disburden himself of his painful secret was as great as that of Perpetua to obtain a knowledge of it; so that, after having repulsed, more and more feebly, her renewed assaults, and after having made her swear many times that she would not breathe a syllable of it, he, with frequent pauses and exclamations, related his miserable adventure. When it was necessary to pronounce the dread name of him from whom the prohibition came, he required from Perpetua another and more solemn oath. Having uttered that name, he threw himself back on his seat with a heavy sigh, and, in a tone of command as well as supplication, exclaimed:

"For the love of Heaven!"

Mercy upon me!" cried Perpetua, "what a wretch, what a tyrant! Does he not fear God?"

"Will you be silent? Or do you want to ruin me completely?"

"Oh! we are here alone; no one can hear us. But what will my poor master do?"

"See there, now," said Don Abbondio in a peevish tone, "see the fine advice you give me! To ask of me what I'll do? What I'll do? As if you were the one in difficulty, and it was for me to help you out!"

"Nay, I could give you my own poor opinion; but then——"

"But—but then, let us know it."

"My opinion would be, that, as every one says our archbishop is a saint, a man of courage, and not to be frightened by an ugly phiz, and who will take pleasure in upholding a priest against one of these tyrants—I should say, and do say, that you had better write him a handsome letter, to inform him as how——"

"Will you be silent? Will you be silent? Is this advice to offer a poor man? When I get a pistol-bullet in my side—God preserve me!—will the archbishop take it out?"

"Ah! pistol-bullets are not given away like sugar-plums; and it were woful if those dogs should bite every time they bark. If a man knows how to show his teeth, and make himself feared, they hold him in respect. We should not have been brought to such a pass, if you had stood upon your rights. Now, by your good leave——"

"Will you be silent?"

"Certainly. But it is true, though, that when the world sees one is always ready, in every encounter, to lower——"

"Will you be silent? Is this the time for such idle talk?"

"Well, well, you'll think of it to-night. But, in the meantime, do not be the first to harm yourself, to destroy your own health. You ought to eat a mouthful."

"I'll think of it," murmured Don Abbondio; "certainly I'll think of it. I must think of it." And he arose, continuing, "No! I'll take nothing, nothing! I've something else to do. Oh that this should have fallen upon me!"

"Swallow this other little drop, at least," said Perpetua, as she poured out more wine. "You know it always does your stomach good."

"Oh! I want other medicine than that—other medicine than that—other medicine than that!"

So saying, he took the light, and muttering, "A pretty business this! To an honest man like me! And to-morrow, what is to be done?" with other like exclamations, he went toward his bedchamber. Having reached the door, he stopped a moment, and before he quitted the room, exclaimed, turning toward Perpetua, with his finger on his lips, "For the love of Heaven, keep silence!"—"*The Betrothed.*"

Antonio Ghislanzoni

On Musical Instruments

The Clarinet

THIS instrument consists of a severe cold in the head, contained in a tube of yellow wood.

The clarinet was not invented by the Conservatory, but by Fate.

A chiropodist may be produced by study and hard work; but the clarinet-player is born, not made.

The citizen predestined to the clarinet has an intelligence which is almost obtuse up to the age of eighteen—a period of incubation, when he begins to feel in his nose the first thrills of his fatal vocation.

After that his intellect—limited even then—ceases its development altogether; but his nasal organ, in revenge, assumes colossal dimensions.

At twenty he buys his first clarinet for fourteen francs; and three months later his landlord gives him notice. At twenty-five he is admitted into the band of the National Guard.

He dies of a broken heart on finding that not one of his three sons shows the slightest inclination for the instrument through which he has blown all his wits.

The Trombone

The man who plays on this instrument is always one who seeks oblivion in its society—oblivion of domestic troubles, or consolation for love betrayed.

Antonio Ghislanzoni

The man who has held a metal tube in his mouth for six months finds himself proof against every illusion.

At the age of fifty he finds that, of all human passions and feelings, nothing is left him but an insatiable thirst.

Later on, if he wants to obtain the position of porter in a gentleman's house, or aspires to the hand of a woman with a delicate ear, he tries to lay aside his instrument, but the taste for loud notes and strong liquors only leaves him with life.

The Harmoniflute

This instrument, on account of the nature of its monotonous sounds and its tremendous plaintiveness, acts on the nerves of those who hear it, and predisposes to melancholy those who play it.

The harmoniflautist is usually tender and lymphatic of constitution, with blue eyes, and eats only white meats and farinaceous food.

If a man, he is called Oscar; those of the other sex are named Adelaide.

At home, he or she is in the habit of bringing out the instrument at dessert, and dinner being over, and the spirits of the family therefore more or less cheerfully disposed, will entertain the company with the "Miserere" in *Il Trovatore,* or some similar melody.

The harmoniflautist weeps easily. After practising on the instrument for fifteen years or so, he or she dissolves altogether, and is converted into a brook.

The Organ

This complicated and majestic instrument is of a clerical character, and destined, by its great volume of sound, to drown the flat singing of clergy and congregation in church.

The organist is usually a person sent into the world for the purpose of making a great noise without undue expenditure of strength, one who wants to blow harder than others without wearing out his own bellows.

At forty he becomes the intimate friend of the parish priest, and the most influential person connected with the church. By dint of repeating the same refrains every day at matins and vespers, he acquires a knowledge of Latin, and gets all the anthems, hymns, and masses by heart. At fifty he marries a devout spinster recommended by the priest.

He makes a kind and good-tempered husband, his only defect in that capacity being his habit of dreaming out loud on the eve of every church festival. On Easter Eve, for instance, he nearly always awakens his wife by intoning, with the full force of his lungs, *Resurrexit!* The good woman, thus abruptly aroused, never fails to answer him with the orthodox *Alleluia!*

At the age of sixty he becomes deaf, and then begins to think his own playing perfection. At seventy he usually dies of a broken heart, because the new priest, who knows not Joseph, instead of asking him to dine at the principal table with the clergy and other church authorities, has relegated him to an inferior place, and the society of the sacristan and the grave-digger.

The Flute

The unhappy man who succumbs to the fascinations of this instrument is never one who has attained the full development of his intellectual faculties. He always has a pointed nose, marries a short-sighted woman, and dies run over by an omnibus.

The flute is the most deadly of all instruments. It requires a peculiar conformation and special culture of the thumb-nail, with a view to those holes which have to be only half closed.

The man who plays the flute frequently adds to his other infirmities a mania for keeping tame weasels, turtle-doves, or guinea-pigs.

The Violoncello

To play the 'cello, you require to have long, thin fingers; but it is still more indispensable to have very long hair falling over a greasy coat-collar.

In case of fire, the 'cellist who sees his wife and his 'cello in danger will save the latter first.

His greatest satisfaction, as a general thing, is that of " making the strings weep." Sometimes, indeed, he succeeds in making his wife and family do the same thing in consequence of a diet of excessive frugality. Sometimes, too, he contrives to make people laugh or yawn, but this, according to him, is the result of atmospheric influences.

He can express, through his loftily attuned strings, all possible griefs and sorrows, except those of his audience and his creditors.

The Drum

An immense apparatus of wood and sheepskin, full of air and of sinister presages. In melodrama the roll of the drum serves to announce the arrival of a fatal personage, an agent of Destiny, in most cases an ill-used husband. Sometimes this funereal rumbling serves to describe silence—sometimes to indicate the depths of the operatic heroine's despair.

The drummer is a serious man, possessed with the sense of his high dramatic mission. He is able, however, to conceal his conscious pride, and sleep on his instrument when the rest of the orchestra is making all the noise it can. In such cases he commissions the nearest of his colleagues to awaken him at the proper moment.

On awaking, he seizes the two drumsticks and begins to beat; but, should his neighbor forget to rouse him, he prolongs his slumbers till the fall of the curtain. Then he shakes himself, perceives that the opera is over, and rubs his eyes. If it happens that the conductor reprimands him for his remissness at the *attack,* he shrugs his shoulders and replies, " Never mind, the tenor died, all the same. A roll of the drum, more or less, what difference would it have made ? "

Paolo Ferrari

Methods of Making a Living

GIORGIO GUGLIELMI, GERTRUDE GUGLIELMI, *and* GIANNI
BARTOLOMEO SENATORI.

Gior. (*making introduction*). My sister Gertrude. My
friend Gianni Bartolomeo Senatori.

Gian. Delighted!

Ger. Very pleased! (*To* GIORGIO.) And what next?

Gior. Oh, nothing! I must get the designs ready for my
new machine. They are to be submitted to-day, and I must
put all the papers and the drawings in proper order. (*Goes
to a table, where he occupies himself in the manner named,
making occasional notes.*)

Gian. (*to* GERTRUDE). Yes, to be sure, I am an old friend
of his, only we had not seen each other for an age. I find my
dear Giorgio rather upset.

Gior. I should like to know what I have to be cheerful
about.

Gian. You don't believe in the proverb: "Heaven helps
the cheerful man."

Gior. I don't believe in Heaven! Besides, you have not
yet proved——

Gian. How a living can be made? Indeed! Just consider my profession and my social position!

Ger. (*to* GIANNI). Have you no employment?

Gian. At your service, madam—none.

Ger. Then you have some pension or allowance?

119

Gian. None.

Ger. None?

Gian. Yours to command. All I can do is to manufacture bad verse, and I have a certain fluency of tongue, and that is how I make my way. But there are no dramas, no trage- dies. Comedy—it's all comedy—funny, you know.

Ger. Well, but what do you do for a living? Pardon me if I am indiscreet.

Gian. Quite the contrary, let me assure you! I go about it in this way: I have divided the city into twelve districts, or sections, whichever you like to call them. Each month I travel one of my districts. This month it happens to be this one.

Ger. Not very rich, this section! None but poor people live here.

Gian. At your service, madam.

Gior. The rich people are less charitable than the poor.

Gian. Very true. What a pity that it's the poor people who are not rich! But they have an advantage—they are not so suspicious; and another—they don't let you wait about in the hall; you go straight in. In the houses of the wealthy it's maddening: porters, butlers, servants—everybody used to judging one by one's appearance.

Ger. And to showing one the door without ceremony.

Gian. Yours to command.

Ger. But tell me what you do.

Gian. I have several systems. One is to provide poetry. Supposing, for instance, there is a wedding, or a new gradu- ate, or a dancer who has made a tremendous hit, or a cele- brated preacher, or a newly elected deputy. I have a son- net that suits them all. It is sufficient to change the last triplet. I have six variations made up for that triplet. It is a six-barreled-revolver sonnet, and can be shot off six times. Now, observe. Both the quatrains consist of philosophical reflections on the sorrows and joys of life; they answer very well for anybody. In the first triplet I come down to particulars. "And thou!" I begin, without mentioning names. "Thou" may belong to any sex or condition; "thou" is equally good for a man and a woman, for old people and young, for a nobleman or a shopkeeper. Thus:

> "And thou, within whose heart are the most pure
>   Virtues gathered; thou, who feel'st the need
> Of aiding e'er the suff'rer pain t'endure—"

This, you see, is suitable for any person, the point being the possession of a beneficent disposition toward the unfortunate. The last triplet is the loaded chamber turning in the revolver. Let us say we have a bride:

> "Enjoy, oh, gentle bride, the splendid crown
>   Due to all shining souls, indeed,
> And from the heavens to thee this day sent down."

Or else:

> "Enjoy, oh, learned youth, the splendid crown
>   Due to all shining souls, indeed,
> And from Academe to thee this day sent down."

Or else, "Enjoy, oh, artist rare"; or else, "Enjoy, oh, scion thou of royal blood"; or else, "Enjoy, oh, worthy burgher"; or else, "Enjoy, oh, orator sublime——"

Ger. And what if you were speaking of some one who had just died?

Gian. At your service, madam. I should say, " Enjoy, oh, gentle heir——"

Ger. Very ingenious!

Gian. Another system I have is to play the electoral agent. I present myself, we will say, to a marquis, a great man of letters, or a banker. I enter with a certain degree of dignity, stretch out my legs as I sit down, and after a brief preamble on the existing need for men of strong, independent character, on the dangers threatening our country's free institutions, I finally inquire, rather mysteriously, " Would you, in short, sir, be willing to be elected senator?" " But," says he, flattered and smiling, " I do not quite understand." And I reply, " Pardon me if I am unable to divulge anything more at present." " Then, perhaps, you have been charged with sounding me?" " I might have been." Note that I say I *might have been,* not that I have been. That would be a lie, and I never tell lies. Then he goes on, " Pardon me, with whom have I the honor of speaking?" " I am Gianni Bartolomeo Senatori. Don't you remember— Turin—Exchange Café—at luncheon, at dinner?" " Ah, yes, of course I remember, my dear Signor Senatori!" Now observe that I never said *I* remembered. That would be a lie. I ask him if he remembers, and he says he does; so it is he who tells a lie. Sometimes it happens that after getting as far as the vestibule I am confronted by a rude domestic, who says, " Not at home!" Then I give the fellow my card, and say, with my nose in the air, " Here, hand this in to your master!" As you already know, my name is Gianni Bartolomeo Senatori. When you are poor you must use your wits. I use my name too. My cards bear my name, only Bartolomeo comes before Gianni, and is abbreviated to *Bar.;* then, after *Gianni* comes with fine flourishes *Sena-*

tori. When the gentleman sees my card, he reads, "*Bar.
Gianni*— Ah, I see—Baron Gianni!" He gets up, and says,
"Baron Gianni, Senator! Bring him in! Bring him in at
once!" And in I go.

Ger. And after you have once got in?

Gian. Oh, at your service, madam.

Ger. (*to* GIORGIO). You see how he does it?

Gior. Yes, he gains his daily bread by daily tricks.

Gian. Now, that is a piece of cruel and unmerited sarcasm.

Gior. Do you mean to say yours are not daily tricks?

Gian. Yes, the tricks are. But the bread is not daily; it
is irregular, and sometimes annoyingly accompanied by cold
water.—"*Signor Lorenzo.*"

The Penalty for Deceived Husbands

RAIMONDO BRAGANZA *and his Son* FEDERICO.

Rai. I know, ninety per cent of the unfaithful wives represent only ninety out of a hundred husbands who deserve
being deceived. But half of them deserve it through a single
mistake they have made—an imprudent choice. And your
case? The remedy? To make up for the first mistake with
all the good sense possible. It is difficult, true, but there
is a certain sword of Damocles which sharpens the wit and
points the will.

Fed. A sword of Damocles?

Rai. Yes, a sword on whose blade a single word stands
inscribed, the little word describing the husband of the

faithless wife. It is the Inquisition of our day. Should the man kill her? Should he forgive her? The law offers him a wash-basin, and when he has washed his hands he is no better off than he was before. Because society makes no allowances, but strikes him with a terrible punishment, which overtakes him and is inflicted on him without his being conscious of it. Nothing changes; no one denies him the usual bow. Quite the contrary, poor fellow! His friends shake hands with him; why not, poor devil? He is always welcome at his club; he is permitted to act as second in duels; he is invited to shoot at pigeons, to belong to racing committees. But the bows and the hand-shakes have an imperceptible touch of irony, the very least tinge of mockery, which is most pronounced when he passes arm in arm with his best friend. The unhappy man feels as though he were in an unhealthy atmosphere; only he does not reflect, he does not stop to give himself an accurate account of his indisposition. Oh, it may be the heat; or it may be the dampness. No, the name of the disease that has smitten him is *ridicule*. A secret has escaped from a bedroom in his house, and has reached the hall; it runs down to the porter's lodge, slips out into the street, and behold! a whole city is whispering it; a whole city conspires not to spoil the poor wretch's comical trustfulness, to form a shield, while laughing and joking, between him and the two fortunate accomplices in this secret of Punchinello's—while Punchinello is the only one ignorant of it.

Fed. Now I must really protest! The Hebrews stoned the unfaithful wife, the Locretians put her eyes out, the English cut her ears off, the Egyptians her nose, and the Romans, forsooth, chopped off her head—and we moderns make fun of the husband! Oh, if the husband has been a libertine or a fool, I agree; but if his wife has found in him youth, love, protection, and a worthy example, then, by God! the fools are they who laugh at him. And I join with the husband in laughing all the more heartily at those apes playing cockatoo! A man of character has no fear of ridicule.

Rai. Which is the same as if you said a man of character need have no fear of sickness.

Fed. So, then, there is ridicule for the innocent husband, and for the wife, and for the lover?

Rai. The same disease for all of them, you may be sure. But what is the use of telling you? It is time wasted!

—*" Ridicule."*

Enrico Castelnuovo

The Pythagorean Problem

"THE Pythagorean Problem!" said Professor Roveni, in a tone of mild sarcasm, as he unfolded a paper which I had extracted, very gingerly, from an urn standing on his desk. Then he showed it to the government inspector who stood beside him, and whispered something into his ear. Finally he handed me the document, so that I might read the question with my own eyes.

"Go up to the blackboard," added the professor, rubbing his hands.

The candidate who had preceded me in the arduous trial, and had got out of it as best he could, had left the schoolroom on tiptoe, and in opening the door let in a long streak of sunshine, which flickered on wall and floor, and in which I had the satisfaction of seeing my shadow. The door closed again, and the room was once more plunged into twilight. It was a stifling day in August, and the great sunblinds of blue canvas were a slight defense against the heat, so that the Venetian shutters had been closed as well. The little light which remained was concentrated on the master's desk and the blackboard, and was, at any rate, sufficient to illuminate my defeat.

"Go to the blackboard and draw the figure," repeated Professor Roveni, perceiving my hesitation.

Tracing the figure was the only thing I knew how to do; so I took a piece of chalk and conscientiously went to work.

I was in no hurry; the more time I took up in this graphic part, the less remained for oral explanation.

But the professor was not the man to lend himself to my innocent artifice.

"Make haste," he said. "You are not going to draw one of Raphael's Madonnas."

I had to come to an end.

"Put in the letters now. Quick! You are not giving specimens of handwriting. Why did you erase that G?"

"Because it is too much like the C which I have made already. I was going to put an H instead of it."

"What a subtle idea!" observed Roveni, with his usual irony. "Have you finished?"

"Yes, sir," said I; adding under my breath, "more's the pity!"

"Come, why are you standing there moonstruck? Enunciate the theorem!"

Then began my sorrows. The terms of the question had escaped my memory.

"In a triangle—" I stammered.

"Go on."

I took courage and said all I knew.

"In a triangle—the square of the hypotenuse is equal to the squares of the other two sides."

"In any triangle?"

"No, no!" suggested a compassionate soul behind me.

"No, sir!" said I.

"Explain yourself. In what sort of triangle?"

"A right-angled triangle," whispered the prompting voice.

"A right-angled triangle," I repeated, like a parrot.

"Silence behind there!" shouted the professor, and then

continued, turning to me, " Then, according to you, the big square is equal to each of the smaller ones? "

Good gracious! the thing was absurd! But I had a happy inspiration.

" No, sir; to both of them added together."

" To the sum, then—say *to the sum.* And you should say *equivalent,* not equal. Now demonstrate."

I was in a cold perspiration—icy cold, despite the tropical temperature. I looked stupidly at the right-angled triangle, the square of the hypotenuse, and its two subsidiary squares; I passed the chalk from one hand to the other and back again, and said nothing, for the very good reason that I had nothing to say.

No one prompted me any more. It was so still you might have heard a pin drop. The professor fixed his gray eyes on me, sparkling with a malignant joy; the government inspector was making notes on a piece of paper. Suddenly the latter respectable personage cleared his throat, and Professor Roveni said in his most insinuating manner, " Well? "

I did not reply.

Instead of at once sending me about my business, the professor tried to imitate the cat which plays with the mouse before tearing it to pieces.

" Perhaps," he sneered, " you are seeking a new solution. I do not say that such may not be found, but we shall be quite satisfied with one of the old ones. Go on. Have you forgotten that you ought to produce the two sides, DE, MF, till they meet? Produce them—go on! "

I obeyed mechanically. The figure seemed to attain a gigantic size, and weighed on my chest like a block of stone.

" Put a letter at the point where they meet—an N. So. And now? "

I remained silent.

"Don't you think it necessary to draw a line down from N through A to the base of the square, BHIC?"

I thought nothing of the kind; however, I obeyed.

"Now you will have to produce the two sides, BH and IC."

Ouf! I could endure it no more.

"Now," the professor went on, "a child of two could do the demonstration. Have you nothing to observe with reference to the two triangles, BAC and NAE?"

As silence only prolonged my torture, I replied laconically, "Nothing."

"In other words, you know nothing at all?"

"I think you ought to have seen that some time ago," I replied, with a calm worthy of Socrates.

"Very good! Very good! Is that the tone you take? And don't you even know that the Pythagorean Problem is also called the Asses' Bridge, because it is just the asses who cannot get over it? You can go. I hope you understand that you have not passed in this examination. That will teach you to read *Don Quixote* and draw cats during my lessons!"

The government inspector took a pinch of snuff. I laid down the chalk and the duster, and walked majestically out of the hall, amid the stifled laughter of my schoolfellows.

Three or four of my comrades who had already gone through the ordeal with no very brilliant result were waiting for me outside.

"So you have failed, eh?"

"Yes, I've failed!" I replied, throwing myself into an attitude of heroic defiance, adding presently, "I always said that mathematics were only made for fools."

"Of course!" exclaimed one of my young friends.

"What question did you have?" asked another.

"The Pythagorean Problem. What can it matter to me whether the square of the hypotenuse is or is not equal to the sum of the squares of the two sides?"

"Of course it can't matter to you—nor to me—nor to any one in the world!" chimed in a third with all the petulant ignorance of fourteen. "If it is equal, why do they want to have it repeated so often? And if it is not, why do they bother us with it?"

"Believe me, you fellows," said I, ending the discussion with the air of a person of long experience, "you may be quite certain of it, our whole system of education is wrong."

—"*Smiles and Tears.*"

Edmondo d'Amicis

The Conscript

AT the end of the courtyard a conscript was sitting alone
on the door-steps, with his elbows resting on his knees and
his chin sunk in his fists. He surveyed his comrades as they
went out one by one, and when they were all gone fixed his
gaze steadfastly to the ground. He looked like one of the
worthy fellows who leave home and family with an aching
heart, yet who come to their soldier's duty with a sense of
necessity and willingness. But there was something more
in his face than the half-bewildered, half-vacant look usually
to be observed in conscripts during their first few days of
service. The man showed a positively doleful countenance.
Perhaps he was sorry he had not gone out with the others.
It is a melancholy thing enough to spend a fine Sunday
moping at home.

A corporal in undress uniform crossing the court observes
the conscript, and confronts him sharply with :

" What are you sitting there for, with your hands doubled
up like that ? "

" I ? " inquires the private.

" I ? " mimics the corporal, with a grimace. " Really, how
remarkable ! Whom do you imagine you are speaking to—
the moon ? Yes, you ! Get up when you address a superior."

The conscript rises.

" Who are you, and what company do you belong to ? "

" Company ? "

" Company ? " again mocks the other. " Are you aware

that you are a regular idiot?" He comes up to the soldier, takes him by the jacket, and, giving him a terrifying tug, exclaims, "Look how you have messed your uniform by sitting on the ground like a beggar!"

The conscript begins to brush off his jacket with his hand.

"Look at the state of your boots!" shouts his superior, bestowing a kick on one of his feet.

The private bends down to dust his boots with his pocket-handkerchief.

"Straighten your necktie; it's all over your ears!" And, seizing him by the necktie, he swings his subordinate round so that he all but falls down.

No sooner does the conscript attempt to arrange the disordered cravat, when he hears the command:

"Put that cap on properly."

Up goes a hand to the cap.

"And hoist up those breeches, if you don't want them to be ruined in a week; smooth the front of your jacket; take out those ridiculous earrings; and don't stand there with your chin buried in your stomach, like a monk! Drop that idiotic stare!"

The unfortunate youth fumbles with trembling fingers now at his cravat, now at his trousers, now at his cap, and now at his jacket, but the more he fumbles the less does he improve things.

Just then the pretty young canteen woman passes by, and stops to look at him—the heartless creature! To appear ridiculous before the eyes of beauty—ah, that is the worst disaster of all! So the poor wretch loses his head altogether, pulls about his necktie and buttons worse than ever, then drops his arms, his chin, and his eyes in succession, until he stands a mute picture of despair. The canteen woman laughs and moves on. The corporal, looking at him in utter contempt, shakes his head, repeating, "You jackass! You jackass!" Then, in a higher-pitched voice:

"Wake up, my good man, and do it quickly, too, or else you will have to be shown how! Bread and water and the lockup first, and then the lockup and bread and water, and so on, change and change about, by way of variety, so that you won't get tired of it. You'd better remember that. Now, then, off to your bedroom and brush your uniform! Forward, march!"

He reenforces this command by pointing with his finger at the dormitory window.

"But I——"

"Silence!"

"I have not——"

"Hold your tongue, will you, when you address a superior! There's the lockup for you, if you don't. Do you see?"

Upon which the corporal swaggers off, mumbling, "Lord, such people! Army's going to the dogs! Italy's going to the dogs!"

"Mister Corporal," timidly remarks the conscript.

The departing one halts, turns, and points menacingly in the direction of the guard-room.

"I wanted to know something, if you please, sir."

The request was made in a tone so respectful and submissive that it was scarcely possible to prohibit him from speaking.

"What is it you want?"

"I just wanted to ask if you knew whether there was an officer from my home here in this regiment. I think there must be, only I don't know if——"

"From your home? If all the people from that place are like you, it's to be hoped you are the only one in the regiment." And, with a shrug of the shoulders, the corporal strode away.—"*Military Life.*"

Tooth for Tooth

An English merchant of Mogador was returning to the city on the evening of a market-day, at the moment when the gate by which he was entering was barred by a crowd of country people driving camels and asses. Although the Englishman called out as loud as he could, "Make way!" an old woman was struck by his horse and knocked down, falling with her face upon a stone. Ill fortune would have it that in the fall she broke her last two front teeth. She was stunned for an instant, and then rose convulsed with rage, and broke out into insults and ferocious maledictions, following the Englishman to his door. She then went before the governor, and demanded that in virtue of the law of talion he should order the English merchant's two front teeth to be broken. The governor tried to pacify her, and advised her to pardon the injury; but she would listen to nothing, and he sent her away with a promise that she should have justice, hoping that when her anger should be exhausted she would herself desist from her pursuit. But, three days having passed, the old woman came back more furious than ever, demanded justice, and insisted that a formal sentence should be pronounced against the Christian.

"Remember," said she to the governor, "thou didst promise me!"

"What!" responded the governor; "dost thou take me for a Christian, that I should be the slave of my word?"

Every day for a month the old woman, athirst for vengeance, presented herself at the door of the citadel, and yelled and cursed and made such a noise, that the governor, to be rid of her, was obliged to yield. He sent for the merchant, explained the case, the right which the law gave the woman, the duty imposed upon himself, and begged him to put an end to the matter by allowing two of his teeth to be removed—any two, although in strict justice they should be two incisors. The Englishman refused absolutely to part with incisors, or eye-teeth, or molars; and the governor was obliged to send the old woman packing, ordering the guard not to let her put her foot in the palace again.

"Very well," said she, "since there are none but degenerate Mussulmans here, since justice is refused to a Mussulman woman against an infidel dog, I will go to the sultan, and we shall see whether the prince of the faithful will deny the law of the Prophet."

True to her determination, she started on her journey alone, with an amulet in her bosom, a stick in her hand, and a bag round her neck, and made on foot the hundred miles which separate Mogador from theh sacred city of the empire. Arrived at Fez, she sought and obtained audience of the sultan, laid her case before him, and demanded the right accorded by the Koran, the application of the law of retaliation. The sultan exhorted her to forgive. She insisted. All the serious difficulties which opposed themselves to the satisfaction of her petition were laid before her. She remained inexorable. A sum of money was offered her, with which she could live in comfort for the rest of her days. She refused it.

"What do I want with your money?" said she; "I am old, and accustomed to live in poverty. What I want is the two teeth of the Christian. I want them; I demand them in the name of the Koran. The sultan, prince of the faithful, head of our religion, father of his subjects, cannot refuse justice to a true believer."

Her obstinacy put the sultan in a most embarrassing position. The law was formal, and her right incontestable; and the ferment of the populace, stirred up by the woman's fanatical declamations, rendered refusal perilous. The sultan, who was Abd-er-Rahman, wrote to the English consul, asking as a favor that he would induce his countryman to allow two of his teeth to be broken. The merchant answered the consul that he would never consent. Then the sultan wrote again, saying that if he would consent he would grant him, in compensation, any commercial privilege that he chose to ask. This time, touched in his purse, the merchant yielded. The old woman left Fez, blessing the name of the pious Abd-er-Rahman, and went back to Mogador, where, in the presence of many people, the two teeth of the Nazarene were broken. When she saw them fall to the ground she gave a yell of triumph, and picked them up with a fierce joy. The merchant, thanks to the privileges accorded him, made in the two following years so handsome a fortune that he went back to England toothless, but happy.

—"*Morocco.*"

Edmondo d'Amicis

Pride

FANCY that Carlo Nobis dusting off his coat-sleeve so disdainfully after Derossi has brushed by him! His infernal pride is simply due to the fact of his father's being a rich man. But Derossi's father is rich too. He thinks he ought to have a whole bench to himself, as if the others would make it unfit for him to sit upon. He gives himself airs, and looks down on everybody. And what a fuss he makes if one of the boys happens to stumble over his foot when we file out of the room! He calls you bad names because of the least thing, or else he threatens to make his father come to the school and complain against you. He deserved the lecture his father gave him for calling the coal-merchant's son a rascally beggar. No one ever saw such a cad. No one cares to speak to him in school, or say good-by when he goes home; there is not even one of us who will whisper an answer to him when he has not learned the lesson. Nobis hates us all, and shows most contempt for Derossi because he is at the head of the class. Garrone he particularly dislikes for the reason that he is so popular. However, Derossi pays no attention to him, and when Garrone hears that Nobis has been blackguarding him behind his back, he says:

"He is so absurdly stuck up that I take no notice of him."

One day Coretti said to him, when he was sneering at his catskin cap:

"Go to Derossi, and ask him to teach you manners."

One day he complained to the master about the Calabrian, who had kicked him on the leg. The master asked the Cala-

137

brian if he had done it on purpose. The reply being a frank
" No, sir," the teacher said to Nobis:

" You are too quick-tempered."

To which Nobis answered, in his haughty fashion:

" I shall tell my father about this."

Now it was for the teacher to get angry:

" If you do, your father will merely point out to you
that you are in the wrong, as he has done before. Besides, it is for no one but the master to judge and punish
in school." And he added, speaking less severely, " Come,
Nobis, try to behave better. Be more civil to your schoolfellows. We have working-men's sons and gentlemen's sons
here, sons of rich parents and sons of poor parents, and they
all love one another and treat each other properly, as they
should. Why don't you behave like the rest? It would be
so easy for you to make the other boys care for you, and
you would be all the happier for it yourself. Well, have you
nothing to answer?"

Nobis, who had been listening with his usual haughty expression, replied coldly:

" No, sir."

" Sit down," said the master. " I am sorry for you. You
seem to have very little heart."

And when Nobis sat down, the little mason on the front
bench turned round and made such an absurd rabbit's face
at him that the whole class burst out laughing. The teacher
saw it, and scolded the boy, but he was obliged to put his
hand up to his mouth to hide a smile. Nobis laughed, too,
but in a very disagreeable way.—" *Cuore.*"

Spanish Wit and Humor

Hurtado de Mendoza

The Cheese-Eating Snake

ONE day, when my wretched, miserable, covetous thief
of a master had gone out, an angel, in the likeness of a tinker,
knocked at the door—for I verily believe he was directed by
Providence to assume that habit and employment—and inquired whether I had anything to mend. Suddenly a light
flashed upon me, as though imparted by an invisible and
unknown power.

"Uncle," said I, "I have unfortunately lost the key of this
great chest, and I'm sadly afraid my master will beat me.
For God's sake, try if you can fit it, and I will reward you."

The angelic tinker drew forth a large bunch of keys and
began to try them, while I assisted his endeavors with my
feeble prayers, when lo, and behold! when least I thought
it, the lid of the chest arose, and I almost fancied I beheld
the divine essence therein in the shape of loaves of bread.
"I have no money," said I to my preserver, "but give me
the key and help yourself."

He took some of the whitest and best bread he could find,
and went away well pleased, though not half so well as
myself.

My wretched master returned, and it pleased God that the
deficiency remained undiscovered by him. The next day,
when he went out, I went to my farinaceous paradise, and,
taking a loaf between my hands and teeth, in a twinkling
it became invisible; then, not forgetting to lock the treasure,
I capered about the house for joy to think that my miserable

139

life was about to change, and for some days following I was as happy as a king. But it was not predestined for me that such good luck should continue long. On the third day I beheld my murderer in the act of examining our chest, turning and counting the loaves over and over again.

After he had been some time considering and counting, he said, "If I were not well assured of the security of this chest, I should say that somebody had stolen my bread; but, however, to remove all suspicion, from this day I shall count the loaves; there remain now exactly nine and a piece."

No sooner did the priest go out than I opened the chest to console myself even with the sight of food, and as I gazed on the nine white loaves a sort of adoration arose within me, which the sight of such tempting morsels could alone inspire. I counted them carefully to see if, perchance, the curmudgeon had mistaken the number; but, alas! I found he was a much better reckoner than I could have desired.

But as hunger increased, and more so in proportion as I had fared better the few days previously, I was reduced to the last extremity. After some consideration, I said within myself, "This chest is very large and old, and in some parts, though very slightly, is broken. It is not impossible to suppose that rats may have made an entrance and gnawed the bread. To take a whole loaf would not be wise, seeing that it would be missed by my most liberal master, but the other plan he shall certainly have the benefit of." Then I began to pick the loaves on some table-cloths which were there, not of the most costly sort, taking one loaf and leaving another, so that in the end I made up a tolerable supply of crums, which I ate like so many sugar-plums; and with that I in some measure consoled myself and contrived to live,

The priest, when he came home to dinner and opened the chest, beheld with dismay the havoc made in his store; but he immediately supposed it to have been occasioned by rats, so well had I imitated the style of those depredators. He examined the chest narrowly, and discovered the little holes through which the rats might have entered, and calling me, he said, " Lazaro, look what havoc has been made with our bread during the night."

I seemed very much astonished, and asked what it could possibly be.

" What has done it? " quoth he; " why, rats, confound 'em! There is no keeping anything from them."

I fared well at dinner, and had no reason to repent of the trick I played, for he pared off all the places which he supposed the rats had nibbled at, and, giving them to me, he said, " There, eat that; rats are very clean animals."

In this manner, adding what I thus gained to that acquired by the labor of my hands, or rather my nails, I managed tolerably well, though I little expected it. I was destined to receive another shock when I beheld my miserable tormentor carefully stopping up all the holes in the chest with small pieces of wood, which he nailed over them, and which bade defiance to further depredations.

Necessity is a great master, and being in this strait, I passed night and day in devising means to get out of it. All the rascally plans that could enter the mind of man did hunger suggest to me, for it is a saying, and a true one, as I can testify, that hunger makes rogues, and abundance fools. One night, when my master slept, of which disposition he always gave sonorous testimony, as I was revolving in my mind the best mode of renewing my intimacy with the contents of the chest, a thought struck me, which I forthwith put in execution. I arose very quietly, and taking an old knife which, having some little glimmering of the same idea the day previous, I had left for an occasion of this nature, I repaired to the chest, and at the part which I considered least guarded I began to bore a hole. The antiquity of the chest seconded my endeavors, for the wood had become rotten from age, and easily yielded to the knife, so that in a short time I managed to display a hole of very respectable dimensions. I then opened the chest very gently, and, taking out the bread, I treated it much in the same manner as heretofore, and then returned safe to my mattress.

When the unhappy priest found his mechanical ability of no avail, he said, "Really, this chest is in such a state, and the wood is so old and rotten, that the rats make nothing of it. The best plan I can think of, since what we have done is of no use, is to arm ourselves within against these cursed rats."

He then borrowed a rat-trap, and baiting it with bits of cheese which he begged from the neighbors, set it under the chest. This was a piece of singular good fortune for me, for although my hunger needed no sauce, yet I did not nibble the bread at night with less relish because I added thereto the bait from the rat-trap. When in the morning he found not only the bread gone as usual, but the bait likewise vanished, and the trap without a tenant, he grew almost beside himself. He ran to the neighbors and asked of them what animal it could possibly be that could positively eat the very cheese out of the trap and yet escape untouched.

The neighbors agreed that it could be no rat that could thus eat the bait and not remain within the trap, and one more cunning than the rest observed, " I remember once seeing a snake about your premises, and depend on it that is the animal which has done you this mischief, for it could easily pick the bait from the trap without entering entirely, and thus, too, it might easily escape." The rest all agreed that such must be the fact, which alarmed my master a good deal.

He now slept not near so soundly as before, and at every little noise, thinking it was the snake biting the chest, he would get up, and taking a cudgel which he kept at his bed's head for the purpose, began to belabor the poor chest with all his might, so that the noise might frighten the reptile from his unthrifty proceedings. He even awoke the neighbors with such prodigious clamor, and I could not get a single minute's rest. He turned me out of bed, and looked among the straw, and about the blanket, to see if the creature was concealed anywhere; for, as he observed, at night they seek warm places, and not infrequently injure people by biting them in bed. When he came I always pretended to be very heavy with sleep, and he would say to me in the morning, " Did you hear nothing last night, boy? The snake was about, and I think I heard him at your bed, for they are very cold creatures, and love warmth."

" I hope to God he will not bite me," returned I, " for I am very much afraid."

He was so watchful at night that, by my faith, the snake could not continue his operations as usual, but in the morning, when the priest was at church, he resumed them pretty steadily as usual.

Looking with dismay at the damage done to his store, and the little redress he was likely to have for it, the poor priest became quite uneasy from fretting, and wandered about all night like a hobgoblin. I began very much to fear that, during one of these fits of watchfulness, he might discover my key, which I placed for security under the straw of my bed. I therefore, with a caution peculiar to my nature, determined in future to keep this treasure by night safe in my mouth.

It was decreed by my evil destiny, or rather, I ought to say, as a punishment for my evil doings, that one night, when I was fast asleep, my mouth being somewhat open, the key became placed in such a position therein that my breath came in contact with the hollow of the key, and caused—worse luck for me—a loud whistling noise. On this my watchful master pricked up his ears, and thought it must be the hissing of the snake which had done him all the damage, and certainly he was not altogether wrong in his conjectures. He arose very quietly, with his club in his hand, and stealing toward the place whence the hissing sound proceeded, thinking at once to put an end to his enemy, he lifted his club, and with all his force discharged such a blow on my unfortunate head that it needed not another to deprive me of all sense and motion. The moment the blow was delivered he felt it was no snake that had received it, and, guessing what he had done, called out to me in a loud voice, endeavoring to recall me to my senses. Then, touching me with his hands, he felt the blood, which was by this time in great profusion about my face, and ran quickly to procure a light. On his return he found me moaning, yet still holding the key in my mouth, and partly visible, being in the same situation which caused the whistling noise he had mistaken for the snake. Without thinking much of me, the attention of the slayer of snakes was attracted by the appearance of the key, and drawing it from my mouth, he soon discovered what it was. He ran to prove it, and with that at once found out the extent of my ingenuity.

Hurtado de Mendoza

"Thank God," exclaimed this cruel snake-hunter, "that the rats and the snakes which have so long made war upon me and devoured my substance, are both at last discovered!"

—"*Lazarillo de Tormes.*"

Lope de Vega

The Demoniac

CHARACTERS:

SARMIENTO.
INES, *his Daughter.*
PEDRO, INES'S *Lover.*

GIL.
PASCUAL. } *Servants.*

A Street.

GIL *and* PASCUAL.

Gil. No, master wiseacre, you had better not engage in
a contest with me; you would be sure to get the worst of it.

Pas. Silence, fool! I contest with you? Your wits are
far from great enough to tempt me to match mine against
them. Everything you say is as complete folly as ever I
heard in my life.

Gil. Folly, it seems to you? Listen to me. Suppose, for
the sake of argument, that I am a hunter, have my musket
slung across my back, and come across country to an inn.
Seven sparrows are sitting on the roof of the inn. I take
aim and kill two. How many remain?

Pas. A question, forsooth, to puzzle wiser heads. If there
were seven sparrows to begin with, and two are killed, five
remain. Surely that's clear!

Gil. Now I'll show you what an ass you are. If I kill
two with my musket, the other five fly off. That's clear
as day!

Pas. To be sure!

Gil. Hence none remain.

Pas. I grant that I'm beaten.

Enter PEDRO.

Gil. Do you see that fellow coming up here? We had better go, for the devil walks abroad. (*Exeunt.*)

Pedro. Thank Heaven they are gone. I can hardly step out into the street without meeting these enemies of my heart; for that they are. It is their master's daughter who, fair as an angel, so fills my soul that I may neither eat nor sleep, but ever like a rocket ascend athwart the sky. It is her wish to speak to me at this hour. Hist! hist, lady!

Ines (*at a window*). Who is there?

Pedro. Who could it be but I—I, whose soul is steeped in adoration of the divine beauty of your eyes!

Ines. Leave compliments aside, and never cross the street again. My father and my brothers have become aware of the way you haunt our house, and it has caused me great annoyance. Therefore, go! Good luck to you, but never return.

Pedro. Is this possible, sweet lady? Can you drive me away thus? I must return! Leave me not so forsaken in the world!

Ines. But what would you have me do? Speak softly, at least, for my father is at home. I have told you—there is no hope left for you.

Pedro. For the blessed saints' sake, I beg you, listen to a few words! That much grace, at least, I deserve.

Ines. Well, you must be quick, and not keep me long. My father may come in at any moment.

147

Pedro. If you will accede to the request I am about to make, I hope to gain entrance to your house by such means that your father himself will introduce me there.

Ines. Let me hear your plan. If it is such that my reputation shall suffer no harm by it, I will gladly help you.

Pedro. Listen, then. You know that recently an exorcist arrived in town—that is to say, one who bans or exorcises demons. In order, now, to gain our end, you have nothing more to do than to behave like one possessed by an evil spirit. The rest you may leave to me. As soon as your condition is observed, the exorcist will be sent for, whose rôle I will assume.

Ines. Heavens! sir, I am to be possessed?

Pedro. Not at all! You are merely to behave as though you were.

Ines. If that is indeed all, I am quite willing to do it.

Pedro. But be very careful not to appear too mad. Only talk somewhat wildly; call upon Venus and Jove; say that you can fly toward heaven; dance, run about, and beat the servants.

Ines. I understand, and I'll begin at once.

Pedro. I am the happiest of men. By hitting upon this plan I shall gain the happiness for which I have so long waited in vain.

A Room in Sarmiento's *House.*

Ines *runs in, behaving as if mad. Behind her come* Sar-miento, Gil, *and* Pascual.

Ines. Come, Venus, Mars, Apollo, Saturn, Jove, Minerva! Do you not recognize me, your sovereign queen? Hither, you dogs! And you, old fellows, come here and answer me!

It was you who drove the devil into me! (*To* GIL.) Away with you, shameless fool! Do not come near me! (*She gives* GIL *a box on the ear.*)

Gil. Oh! oh!

Sar. But what is the meaning of all this? What can be the matter with my daughter?

Pas. Sir, she is possessed of a demon. That seems clear as day. Everything she says and does points to that.

Sar. Come here! Which of you knows where the exorcist lives who recently came here?

Gil. I know, sir.

Sar. Then hurry off to him, summon him, or, if possible, bring him, for we have urgent need of him.

Gil. I hasten.   (*Exit.*)

Ines. I would fly into the air! Toward heaven—toward heaven!

Sar. Be quiet, daughter; do not frighten me so.

Ines. Out upon you, you pack of thieves, you despoilers of my felicity! Do not torture my soul! Let me follow the happiness that you would keep from me!

Enter GIL *with* PEDRO, *who is disguised as an exorcist.*

Pedro. Where is *mulier,* who has *dæmonios in corpore suo?*

Sar. Good exorcist, you are heartily welcome! I pray you, for God's sake, to heal my daughter.

Ines. Oh, thou delight of mine eyes! Do thou come, and do as thou hast said.

Pedro. Take note! that is the devil speaking in her, to whom it is necessary to reply in similar fashion.—Yes, thou beloved of my soul, I come! I come! If thou will it, re-

main but true to thy promise. I am faithful even unto death!
—Now, however, in order to bring about a cure, it is necessary that all present blindfold themselves. For it is a rule
of Aristotle: *Nihil baccum cum ataro.*

Sar. Quick, you fellows, bind your eyes!

(All blindfold themselves.)

*Pedro. Dæmonius maledictus, quæ intrabit corpore mulier,
et tentabit* this woman, *exi,* get out!

Gil. Open your mouth, mistress! He wants to tear out
the devil.

Pedro. Silence, beast! Let me perform my office, and
do not disturb me.

Sar. Away with you, rascal! Do not interrupt the gentleman in his business.

Pedro. By the power I have over you, I exorcise you, and
command you to leave the body of this maiden forthwith!

Ines. Oh! Oh!

Pedro. Silence! Silence! There comes the demon out of
her body. Do you not see him?

Gil. To be sure! He almost knocked me down.

Sar. Into whom did the demon pass?

Gil. Into the Great Mogul.

Pedro. So far has the cure been effected. The devil has
been driven forth. But in order that your daughter be entirely made whole, it is necessary that I remain here for a
space of twenty or thirty days; for she is still weak and
exhausted, and for that reason likewise needs strengthen-
ing food.

Sar. Upon my faith, sir, could I have my way, you should
not remain thirty days, but as many months in my house.—

You servants, bring my daughter something to eat, and carry
out all the commands of this gentleman as though they were
my own.—Now, sir, come to the refectory, and let me entertain you as befits your great service to us.

(Exeunt SARMIENTO, PEDRO, *and* INES.)

Gil. But tell me, does one feed those who are possessed?

Pas. Why, don't you understand that, idiot? They are
fed because the tortures of the possessing demon weaken
and emaciate them.

Gil. Well, then, if they are fed that way, devil take me
but I'll be possessed too!

Pas. What do you say, fool?

Gil. Mind your own business! Haven't I as good a right
to be possessed as any one else? Watch me: I'll come tearing in, too, and call Venus, Mars, Apollo, Jupiter!

Pas. For my part you may do it, and I'll even promise
not to betray you—on one condition: that you give me half
of all you get.

Gil. Be it so! Come on!   *(Exit.)*

Pas. No, you go first; I'll stay here. A droll idea that
the fool has hit upon!

Enter PEDRO.

Pedro. Can mortal man be happier than I?

Pas. Well, sir, how is my mistress?

Pedro. Far better and much calmer.

Gil. (screams behind the scenes). To heaven, to heaven
I must fly! There are only two miles more!

Pedro. What's that?

Pas. Since you ask me, sir, I'll tell you. This silly fellow, Gil, heard that, since our mistress is possessed, she is to

be well fed, and so he feigns to be equally afflicted, in the hope of similar fare. He made a fool of me to-day. Here is my chance of revenge.

Pedro. Just leave him to me. I'll play a trick on him that he'll remember long. Bring me a stick and a rope, and then leave me alone with him.

Pas. Good! (*He brings the desired things, and goes.*)

Gil. (*runs in wildly*). Venus, Jupiter, Apollo! Do you not recognize in me him who must beat you all?

Pedro. Ah, accursed demon, what would you?

Gil. Food, sir, food!

Pedro. Kiss the cross, accursed demon!

Gil. Nay, I am a devil who flies out only at the sight of a piled-up dish of cabbage and turnips.

Pedro. Quot legiones!

Gil. Things baked and roasted and boiled; chickens and patties in legions!

Pedro. Dog of a demon, I know you! Kneel! I will punish you as you deserve. (Gil *kneels, and* Pedro *binds his hands.*) *Dæmonius quod petis?* What would you?

Gil. Food! Food!

Pedro. Nay, because you tempted poor Benito recently, you shall fast for thirty days.

Gil. Are you in your right mind, master exorcist? I believe you have too much wine in your head.

Pedro. Nothing can shake my determination. You must fast for a month!

Gil. But listen to reason! I am not possessed at all.

Pedro. Nay, vile devil, you cannot escape my power by such tricks. What would you?

Gil. Food!

Pedro. Food? Well, here you have something to satisfy you!   *(He beats him with the stick. Then exit.)*

Pas. (enters). Let me see how Gil is faring, and whether the exorcist has healed him.—But here he is! Why, how now, Gil? You are bound!

Gil. Yes, they bound me because I ate too much. I have eaten so much that I could not swallow another bite. But, for Heaven's sake, free me from these bonds!

Pas. So! Now let's be off!

Gil. No, not yet. First I must give you the half of what I received.

Pas. Let be! You may have both halves. I give you my share.

Gil. Oh, no! I'll stand by the agreement!

                              (GIL *flogs* PASCUAL.)

Luis de Gongora

Truth and Falsehood

Riches will serve for titles too;
That's true—that's true!
They love most who oftener sigh;
That's a lie—that's a lie!

That crowns give virtue, power gives wit;
That follies well on proud men sit;
That poor men's slips deserve a halter,
While honors deck the *great* defaulter;
That 'nointed kings no wrong can do,
No right such worms as I and you,
That's true—that's true!

To say a dull and sleepy warden
Can watch a many-portal'd garden;
That woes which darken many a day,
One moment's smile can charm away;
To say you think that Celia's eye
Speaks aught but trick and treachery,
That's a lie—that's a lie!

That wisdom's bought and virtue sold,
And that you can provide with gold
For fame a garter or a star,
And valor fit for peace or war,

Luis de Gongora

And purchase knowledge at the U-
Niversity for P. or Q.,
That's true—that's true!

They must be gagged who go to court,
And bless, besides, the gagger for't;
The rank-less must be scourged, and thank
The scourgers when they're men of rank;
The humble poor man's form and hue
Deserve both shame and suffering too,
That's true—that's true!

But splendid favors to be done,
And glorious prizes to be won,
And downy pillows for our head,
And thornless roses for our bed,
From monarchs' words—you'll trust and try,
And risk your honor on the die—
That's a lie—that's a lie!

Baltasar del Alcazar

Sleep

SLEEP is no servant of the will;
  It has caprices of its own;
  When most pursued, 'tis swiftly gone;
When courted least, it lingers still.
With its vagaries long perplext,
  I turned and turned my restless sconce,
  Till, one fine night, I thought at once
I'd master it. So hear my text.

When sleep doth tarry, I begin
  My long and well-accustomed prayer,
  And in a twinkling sleep is there,
Through my bed-curtains peeping in.
When sleep hangs heavy on my eyes,
  I think of debts I fain would pay,
  And then, as flies night's shade from day,
Sleep from my heavy eyelids flies.

And, thus controlled, the winged one bends
  E'en his fantastic will to me,
  And, strange yet true, both I and he
Are friends—the very best of friends.
We are a happy wedded pair,
  And I the lord and he the dame;
  Our bed, our board, our dreams the same,
And we're united everywhere,

Baltasar del Alcazar

I'll tell you where I learned to school
  This wayward sleep: a whispered word
  From a church-going hag I heard,
And tried it, for I was no fool.
So, from that very hour I knew
  That, having ready prayers to pray,
  'And having many debts to pay,
Will serve for sleep, and waking too.

Miguel Cervantes

The Attack on the Windmills

THEY came in sight of thirty or forty windmills standing in the plain; and as soon as Don Quixote espied them, he said to his squire:

"Fortune disposes our affairs better than we ourselves could have desired. Look yonder, friend Sancho Panza, where thou mayest discover somewhat more than thirty monstrous giants, whom I intend to encounter and slay, and with their spoils we will begin to enrich ourselves; for it is lawful war, and doing God good service, to remove so wicked a generation from off the face of the earth."

"What giants?" said Sancho Panza.

"Those thou seest yonder," answered his master, "with their long arms; for some are wont to have them almost of the length of two leagues."

"Look, sir," answered Sancho, "those which appear yonder are not giants, but windmills, and what seem to be arms are the sails, which, whirled about by the wind, make the millstone go."

"It is very evident," answered Don Quixote, "that thou art not versed in the business of adventures. They are giants; and if thou art afraid, get thee aside and pray, while I engage with them in fierce and unequal combat."

So saying, he clapped spurs to his steed, notwithstanding the cries his squire sent after him, assuring him that they were certainly windmills, and not giants. But he was so fully possessed that they were giants, that he neither heard the outcries of his squire Sancho, nor yet discerned what they were, though he was very near them, but went on, crying out aloud, "Fly not, ye cowards and vile caitiffs! It is a single knight who assaults you."

The wind now rising a little, the great sails began to move, upon which Don Quixote called out:

"Although ye should have more arms than the giant Briareus, ye shall pay for it!"

Thus recommending himself devoutly to his lady Dulcinea, beseeching her to succor him in the present danger, being well covered with his buckler and setting his lance in the rest, he rushed on as fast as Rozinante could gallop and attacked the first mill before him, when, running his lance into the sail, the wind whirled it about with so much violence that it broke the lance to shivers, dragging horse and rider after it, and tumbling them over and over on the plain in very evil plight. Sancho Panza hastened to his assistance as fast as the ass could carry him; and when he came up to his master he found him unable to stir, so violent was the blow which he and Rozinante had received in their fall.

"God save me!" quoth Sancho, "did not I warn you to have a care of what you did, for that they were nothing but windmills? And nobody could mistake them but one that had the like in his head."

"Peace, friend Sancho," answered Don Quixote; "for matters of war are, of all others, most subject to continual change. Now I verily believe, and it is most certainly the fact, that the sage Freston, who stole away my chamber and books, has metamorphosed these giants into windmills, on purpose to deprive me of the glory of vanquishing them, so great is the enmity he bears me! But his wicked arts will finally avail but little against the goodness of my sword."

"God grant it!" answered Sancho Panza. Then, helping him to rise, he mounted him again upon his steed, which was almost disjointed.—"*Don Quixote.*"

Great Battle Against a Flock of Sheep

WHILE the knight and his squire were conferring together, Don Quixote perceived in the road on which they were traveling a great and thick cloud of dust coming toward them; upon which he turned to Sancho, and said:

"This is the day, oh, Sancho, that shall manifest the good that fortune hath in store for me. This is the day, I say, on which shall be proved, as at all times, the valor of my arm, and on which I shall perform exploits that will be recorded and written in the book of fame, and there remain to all succeeding ages. Seest thou that cloud of dust, Sancho? It is raised by a prodigious army of divers and innumerable nations, who are on the march this way."

"If so, there must be armies," said Sancho; "for here, on this side, arises just such another cloud of dust."

Don Quixote turned, and seeing that it really was so he rejoiced exceedingly, taking it for granted there were two armies coming to engage in the midst of that spacious plain; for at all hours and moments his imagination was full of the battles, enchantments, adventures, extravagances, amours, and challenges detailed in his favorite books, and in every thought, word, and action he reverted to them. Now, the cloud of dust he saw was raised by two great flocks of sheep going the same road from different parts, and as the dust concealed them until they came near, and Don Quixote affirmed so positively that they were armies, Sancho began to believe it, and said, " Sir, what then must we do? "

" What? " replied Don Quixote. " Favor and assist the weaker side! Thou must know, Sancho, that the army which marches toward us in front is led and commanded by the great Emperor Alifanfaron, lord of the great island of Taprobana; this other, which marches behind us, is that of his enemy, the King of the Garamantes, Pentapolin of the Naked Arm, for he always enters into battle with his right arm bare."

" But why do these two princes bear one another so much ill will? " demanded Sancho.

" They hate one another," answered Don Quixote, " because this Alifanfaron is a furious pagan, in love with the daughter of Pentapolin, who is a most beautiful and superlatively graceful lady, and also a Christian; but her father will not give her in marriage to the pagan king unless he will first renounce the religion of his false prophet Mohammed, and turn Christian."

" By my beard," said Sancho, " Pentapolin is in the right; and I am resolved to assist him to the utmost of my power."

" Therein thou wilt do thy duty, Sancho," said Don Quixote; " for, in order to engage in such contests, it is not necessary to be dubbed a knight."

" I easily comprehend that," answered Sancho. " But where shall we dispose of this ass, that we may be sure to find him when the fray is over? For I believe it was never yet the fashion to go to battle on a beast of this kind."

" Thou art in the right," said Don Quixote; " and thou mayest let him take his chance whether he be lost or not, for we shall have such choice of horses after the victory, that Rozinante himself will run a risk of being exchanged. But listen with attention while I give thee an account of the principal knights in the two approaching armies; and that thou mayest observe them the better, let us retire to that rising ground, whence both armies may be distinctly seen."

They did so, and placed themselves for that purpose on a hillock, from which the two flocks which Don Quixote mistook for armies might easily have been discerned, had not their view been obstructed by the clouds of dust. Seeing, however, in his imagination what did not exist, he began with a loud voice to say:

" The knight thou seest yonder with the gilded armor, who bears on his shield a lion crowned, *couchant* at a damsel's feet, is the valorous Laurcalco, Lord of the Silver Bridge. The other, with the armor flowered with gold, who bears the three crowns *argent* in a field *azure,* is the formidable Micocolembo, Grand Duke of Quiracia. The third, with gigantic limbs, who marches on his right, is the undaunted Brandabarbaran of Boliche, Lord of the Three Arabias. He is armed with a serpent's skin, and bears instead of a shield, a gate, which fame says is one of those belonging to the temple which Samson pulled down when with his death he avenged himself upon his enemies. But turn thine eyes on this other side, and there thou wilt see, in front of this other army, the ever-victorious and never-vanquished Timonel de Carcajona, Prince of the New Biscay, who comes clad in armor quartered *azure, vert, argent,* and *or;* bearing on his shield a car *or* in a field *gules,* with a scroll inscribed MIAU, being the beginning of his mistress's name, who, it is reported, is the peerless Miaulina, daughter of Alphenniquen, Duke of Algarve. That other who burdens and oppresses the back of yon powerful steed, whose armor is as white as snow, and his shield also white, without any device, is a new knight, by birth a Frenchman, called Peter Papin, Lord of the Baronies of Utrique. The other whom thou seest, with his armed heels pricking the flanks of that fleet piebald courser, and his armor of pure azure, is the mighty Duke of Nerbia, Espartafilardo of the Wood, whose device is an asparagus-bed, with this motto in Castilian, ' Thus drags my fortune.' "

In this manner he went on naming sundry knights of each squadron, as his fancy dictated, and giving to each their arms, colors, devices, and mottoes extempore; and, without pausing, he continued thus:

"That squadron in the front is formed and composed of people of different nations. Here stand those who drink the sweet waters of the famous Xanthus; the mountaineers who tread the Massilian fields; those who sift the pure and fine gold-dust of Arabia Felix; those who dwell along the famous and refreshing banks of the clear Thermodon; those who drain, by divers and sundry ways, the golden veins of Pactolus; the Numidians, unfaithful in their promises, the Persians, famous for bows and arrows; the Parthians and Medes, who fight flying; the Arabians, perpetually changing their habitations; the Scythians, as cruel as fair; the broad-lipped Ethiopians; and an infinity of other nations, whose countenances I see and know, although I cannot recollect their names. In that other squadron come those who drink the crystal streams of olive-bearing Betis; those who brighten and polish their faces with the liquor of the ever rich and golden Tagus; those who enjoy the beneficial waters of the divine Genil; those who tread the Tartesian fields, abounding in pasture; those who recreate themselves in the Elysian meads of Xereza; the rich Manchegans, crowned with yellow ears of corn; those clad in iron, the antique remains of the Gothic race; those who bathe themselves in Pisuerga, famous for the gentleness of its current; those who feed their flocks on the spacious pastures of the winding Guadiana, celebrated for its hidden source; those who shiver on the cold brow of the woody Pyreneus and the snowy tops of lofty Appeninus; in a word, all that Europe contains and includes."

Good Heaven, how many provinces did he name, how many nations did he enumerate, giving to each, with wonderful readiness, its peculiar attributes! Sancho Panza stood confounded at his discourse, without speaking a word; and now and then he turned his head about to see whether he could discover the knights and giants his master named. But, seeing none, he said:

" Sir, the devil a man, or giant, or knight, of all you have named, can I see anywhere; perhaps all may be enchantment, like last night's goblins."

" How sayest thou, Sancho?" answered Don Quixote. " Hearest thou not the neighing of the steeds, the sound of the trumpets, and the rattling of the drums?"

" I hear nothing," answered Sancho, " but the bleating of sheep and lambs."

And so it was, for now the two flocks were come very near them.

" Thy fears, Sancho," said Don Quixote, " prevent thee from hearing or seeing aright; for one effect of fear is to disturb the senses and make things not to appear what they really are; and if thou art so much afraid, retire, and leave me alone, for with my single arm I shall insure victory to that side which I favor with my assistance." Then, clapping spurs to Rozinante and setting his lance in rest, he darted down the hillock like lightning. Sancho cried out to him:

"Hold, my Lord Don Quixote—come back! As God shall save me, they are lambs and sheep you are going to encounter! Pray come back! Wo to the father that begot me! What madness is this! Look: there is neither giant nor knight, nor cats, nor arms, nor shields quartered nor entire, nor true azures nor bedeviled! Sinner that I am! What are you doing?"

Notwithstanding all this, Don Quixote turned not again, but still went on, crying aloud:

"Ho, knights! You that follow and fight under the banner of the valiant Emperor Pentapolin of the Naked Arm, follow me all, and you shall see with how much ease I revenge him on his enemy Alifanfaron of Taprobana!"

With these words he rushed into the midst of the squadron of sheep, and began to attack them with his lance as courageously and intrepidly as if in good earnest he was engaging his mortal enemies. The shepherds and herdsmen who came with the flocks called out to him to desist; but seeing it was to no purpose, they unbuckled their slings and began to salute his ears with a shower of stones. Don Quixote cared not for the stones, but, galloping about on all sides, cried out:

"Where art thou, proud Alifanfaron? Present thyself before me! I am a single knight, desirous to prove thy valor hand to hand, and to punish thee with the loss of life for the wrong thou dost to the valiant Pentapolin Garamanta!"

At that instant a large stone struck him with such violence on the side that it bent a couple of ribs in his body; insomuch that he believed himself either slain or sorely wounded; and therefore, remembering his balsam, he pulled out the cruse, and, applying it to his mouth, began to swallow some of the liquor; but before he could take what he thought sufficient, another of those almonds hit him full on the hand and dashed the cruse to pieces, knocking out three or four of his teeth, by the way, and grievously bruising two of his fingers. Such was the first blow, and such the second, that the poor knight fell from his horse to the ground. The shepherds ran to him, and verily believed they had killed him; whereupon in all haste they collected their flock, took up their dead, which were about seven, and marched off without further inquiry.—"*Don Quixote.*"

Rascalities of Rincon and Cortado

At the hostelry of the Mulinillo, which is situate on the confines of the renowned plain of Alcudia, and on the road from Castile to Andalusia, two striplings met by chance on one of the hottest days of summer. One of them was about fourteen or fifteen years of age; the other could not have passed his seventeenth year. Both were well formed and of comely features, but in very ragged and tattered plight. Cloaks they had none; their breeches were of linen, and their stockings were merely those bestowed on them by nature. It is true they boasted shoes; one of them wore sandals of cord, or rather dragged them along at his heels; the other had what might as well have been shackles, for all the good they did the wearer, being rent in the uppers, and without soles. Their respective head-dresses were a tiny round cap and a shabby hat with wide, flapping brim, low in the crown. On his shoulder, and crossing his breast like a scarf, one of them carried a shirt the color of chamois leather; the body of this garment was rolled up and thrust into one of its sleeves. The other, though traveling without encumbrance, bore on his chest what seemed a large pack, but which proved, on closer inspection, to be the remains of a starched ruff, now stiffened with grease instead of starch, and so worn and frayed that it looked like a bundle of hemp.

Within this collar, wrapped up and carefully treasured, was a pack of cards, excessively dirty, and reduced to an oval form by repeated paring of their dilapidated corners. The lads were both much burned by the sun, their hands were anything but clean, and their long nails were edged with black. One had a dudgeon-dagger by his side, the other a knife with a yellow handle.

These gentlemen had selected for a nap the porch or penthouse commonly found before an inn; and finding themselves opposite each other, he who appeared to be the elder said to the younger:

" Of what country is your Worship, noble sir, and by what road do you propose to travel?"

" What is my country, sir Cavalier," returned the other, " I know not, nor yet which way my road lies."

" Your Worship, however, does not appear to have come from heaven," rejoined the elder; " and as this is not a place wherein a man can take up his abode for good, you must, of necessity, be going farther."

" That is true," replied the younger. " I have, nevertheless, told you only the veritable fact; for as to my country, it is mine no more, since all that belongs to me there is a father who does not consider me his child, and a stepmother who treats me like a son-in-law. With regard to my road, it is that which chance places before me, and it will end where-ever I may find some one who will give me the wherewithal to sustain this miserable life of mine."

"Is your Worship acquainted with any craft?" inquired the first speaker.

"With none," returned the other, "except that I can run like a hare, leap like a goat, and handle a pair of scissors with great dexterity."

"These things are all very good, useful, and profitable," rejoined the elder. "You will readily find the sacristan of some church who will give your Worship the offering-bread of All Saints' Day, for cutting him his paper flowers for Holy Thursday."

"But that is not my manner of cutting," replied the younger. "My father, who, by God's mercy, is a tailor and hose-maker, taught me to cut out that kind of spatterdashes which cover the fore part of the leg and come down over the instep. These I can cut out in such style, that I could pass an examination for the rank of master in the craft; but my ill luck keeps my talents in obscurity."

"The common lot, sir, of able men," replied the first speaker, "for I have always heard that it is the way of the world to let the finest talents go to waste. But your Worship is still at an age when this evil fortune may be remedied, and the rather since, if I mistake not, and my eyes do not deceive me, you have other advantageous qualities which it is your pleasure to keep secret."

"It is true that I have such," returned the younger gentleman, "but they are not of a character to be publicly proclaimed, as your Worship has very judiciously observed."

"But I," rejoined the elder, "may with confidence assure you that I am one of the most discreet and prudent persons to be found within many a league. In order to induce your

Worship to open your heart and repose your faith in my honor, I will enlist your sympathies by first laying bare my own bosom; for I imagine that fate has not brought us together without some hidden purpose. Nay, I believe that we are to be true friends from this day to the end of our lives.

"I, then, your Lordship, am a native of Fuenfrida, a place very well known, indeed renowned for the illustrious travelers who are constantly passing through it. My name is Pedro del Rincon; my father is a person of quality, and a minister of the Holy Crusade, since he holds the important charge of selling indulgences. I was for some time his assistant in that office, and acquitted myself so well, that in all things concerning the sale of indulgences or bulls I could hold my own with any man, though he had the right to consider himself the most accomplished in the profession. But one day, having placed my affections on the money produced by the bulls rather than on the bulls themselves, I took a bag of crowns to my arms, and we two departed together for Madrid.

"In that city, such are the facilities that offer themselves, I soon gutted my bag, and left it with as many wrinkles as a bridegroom's pocket-handkerchief. The person who was charged with the collection of the money hastened to track my steps. I was caught, and met with but scant indulgence. Only, in consideration of my youth, their worships the judges contented themselves with introducing me to the acquaintance of the whipping-post, to have the flies whisked from my shoulders for a certain time, and commanding me to abstain from revisiting the court and capital during a period of four years. I took the matter coolly, bent my shoulders to the operation performed at their command, and made so much haste to begin my prescribed term of exile, that I had no time to pro-

cure sumpter-mules, but contented myself with selecting
from my valuables such as seemed most important and
useful.

"I did not fail to include this pack of cards among them "
—here the speaker exhibited that oviform specimen already
mentioned—" and with these I have gained my bread among
the inns and taverns between Madrid and this place, by playing at Vingt-et-un. It is true they are somewhat soiled and
worn, as your Worship sees; but for him who knows how to
handle them, they possess a marvelous virtue, which is, that
you never cut them but you find an ace at the bottom. If
your Worship, then, is acquainted with the game, you will
see what an advantage it is to know for certain that you have
an ace to begin with, since you may count it either for one
or eleven; and so you may be pretty sure that when the
stakes are laid at twenty-one, your money will be much disposed to stay at home.

"In addition to this, I have acquired the knowledge of
certain mysteries regarding Lansquenet and Reversis, from
the cook of an ambassador who shall be nameless; insomuch
that, even as your Worship might pass as master in the cutting of spatterdashes, so could I, too, take my degree in the
art of flat-catching.

"With all these acquirements, I am tolerably sure of not
dying from hunger, since, even in the most retired farmhouse
I come to, there is always some one to be found who will
not refuse himself the recreation of a few moments at cards.
We have but to make a trial where we are. Let us spread
the net, and it will go hard with us if some bird out of all
the muleteers standing about do not fall into it. I mean to
say, that if we two begin now to play at Vingt-et-un as
though we were in earnest, some one will probably desire to

make a third, and in that case he shall be the man to leave his money behind him."

"With all my heart," replied the younger lad; "and I consider that your Excellency has done me a great favor by communicating to me the history of your life. You have thereby made it impossible for me to conceal mine, and I will hasten to relate it as briefly as possible. Here it is, then:

"I was born at Pedroso, a village situate between Salamanca and Medina del Campo. My father is a tailor, as I have said, and taught me his trade. But from cutting with the scissors I proceeded—my natural abilities coming in aid —to the cutting of purses. The dull, mean life of the village, and the unloving conduct of my mother-in-law, were, besides, but little to my taste. I quitted my birthplace, therefore, repaired to Toledo to exercise my art, and succeeded in it to admiration; for there is not a reliquary suspended to the dress, not a pocket, however carefully concealed, but my fingers shall probe its contents, or my scissors snip it off, though the owner were guarded by the eyes of Argus.

"During four months I spent in Toledo I was never trapped between two doors, nor caught in the fact, nor pursued by the runners of justice, nor blown upon by an informer. It is true that, a week ago, a police spy did set forth my distinguished abilities to the magistrate, and the latter, taking a fancy to me from his description, desired to make my acquaintance; but I am a modest youth, and do not wish to frequent the society of personages so important. Wherefore I took pains to excuse myself from visiting him, and departed in so much haste that I, like yourself, had no time to procure sumpter-mules or small change—nay, I could not even find a return-chaise, nor so much as a cart."

"Console yourself for these omissions," replied Pedro del

Rincon; "and since we now know each other, let us drop these grand and stately airs, and confess frankly that we have not a blessed farthing between us, nor even shoes to our feet."

"Be it so," returned Diego Cortado, for so the younger boy called himself. "Be it so; and since our friendship, as your Worship is pleased to say, is to last our whole lives, let us begin it with solemn and laudable ceremonies." Saying which, Cortado rose to his feet and embraced the Rincon, who returned the compliment with equal tenderness and emotion.

They then began to play at Vingt-et-un with the cards above described, which were certainly free from the royal excise stamp, but by no means free from grease and knavery; and after a few deals Cortado could turn up an ace as well as Rincon his master. When things had attained this point, it chanced that a muleteer came out at the porch, and, as Rincon had anticipated, he soon proposed to make a third in their game.

To this they willingly agreed, and in less than half an hour they had won from him twelve reals and twenty-two mara-vedis, which he felt as sorely as twelve stabs with a dagger and twenty-two thousand sorrows. Presuming that the young chaps would not venture to defend themselves, he thought to get back his money by force; but the two friends laying hands promptly, the one on his dudgeon-dagger and the other on his yellow-handled knife, gave the muleteer so much to do, that if his companions had not hastened to assist him he would have come badly out of the quarrel.

At that moment there chanced to pass by a company of travelers on horseback, who were going to take their nap at another hostelry about half a league farther on. Seeing

the affray between the muleteer with two boys, they inter-
posed, and offered to take the latter in their company to
Seville, if they were going to that city.

"That is exactly where we desire to go," exclaimed Rincon, "and we will serve your Worships in all that it shall
please you to command." Whereupon, without more ado,
they departed with the travelers, leaving the muleteer de-
spoiled of his money and furious with rage, while the hostess
was in great admiration of the finished education and accom-
plishments of the two rogues, whose dialogue she had heard
from beginning to end, while they were not aware of her
presence.

When the hostess told the muleteer that she had heard
the boys say the cards they played with were false, the man
tore his beard for rage, and would have followed them to
the other inn, in the hope of recovering his property; for
he declared it to be a serious affront, and a matter touching
his honor, that two boys should have cheated a grown man
like him. But his companions dissuaded him from doing
what they declared would be nothing better than publishing
his own folly and gullibility; and their arguments, although
they did not console the muleteer, were sufficient to make him
remain where he was.

Meanwhile Cortado and Rincon displayed so much zeal
and readiness in the service of the travelers, that the latter
gave them a lift behind them for the greater part of the way.
They might many a time have rifled the portmanteaus of
their temporary masters, but did not, lest they should thereby
lose the happy opportunity of seeing Seville, in which city
they greatly desired to exercise their talents. Nevertheless,
as they entered Seville—which they did at the hour of evening prayer, and by the gate of the custom-house, on account

of the dues to be paid and the trunks to be examined—Cortado could not refrain from making an examination, on his own account, of the valise which a Frenchman of the company carried with him on the croup of his mule. With his yellow-handled weapon, therefore, he gave it so deep and broad a wound in the side that its very entrails were exposed to view; and he dexterously drew forth two good shirts, a sun-dial, and a memorandum-book, things that did not greatly please him when he had leisure to examine them. Thinking that, since the Frenchman carried that valise on his own mule, it must needs contain matters of more importance than those he had captured, Cortado would fain have looked further into it, but he abstained, as it was probable that the deficiency had been already discovered and the remaining effects secured. Before performing this feat the friends had taken leave of those who had fed them on their journey, and the following day they sold the two shirts in the old-clothes market, which is held at the gate of the arsenal, obtaining twenty reals for their booty.

Having despatched this business, they went to see the city, and admired the great magnificence and vast size of its principal church, and the vast concourse of people on the quays, for it happened to be the season for loading the fleet. There were also six galleys on the water, at sight of which the friends could not refrain from sighing, as they thought the day might come when they should be clapped on board one of those vessels for the remainder of their lives. They remarked the large number of basket-boys, porters, etc., who went to and fro about the ships, and inquired of one among them what sort of a trade it was—whether it was very laborious, and what were the gains.

An Asturian, of whom they made the inquiry, gave answer

to the effect that the trade was a very pleasant one, since they had no harbor dues to pay, and often found themselves at the end of the day with six or seven reals in their pocket, with which they might eat, drink, and enjoy themselves like kings. Those of his calling, he said, had no need to seek a master to whom security must be given, and you could dine when and where you please, since, in the city of Seville, there is not an eating-house, however humble, where you will not find all you want at any hour of the day.

The account given by the Asturian was by no means discouraging to the two friends, neither did his calling seem amiss to them; nay, rather, it appeared to be invented for the very purpose of enabling them to exercise their own profession in secrecy and safety, on account of the facilities it offered for entering houses. They consequently determined to buy such things as were required for the instant adoption of the new trade, especially as they could enter upon it without undergoing any previous scrutiny.

In reply to their further inquiries, the Asturian told them that it would be sufficient if each had a small porter's bag of linen, either new or second-hand, so it was but clean, with three palm-baskets, two large and one small, wherein to carry the meat, fish, and fruit purchased by their employers, while the bag was to be used for carrying the bread. He took them to where all these things were sold; they supplied themselves out of the plunder of the Frenchman, and in less than two hours they might have been taken for regular graduates in their new profession, so deftly did they manage their baskets and so jauntily carry their bags. Their instructor, furthermore, informed them of the different places at which they were to make their appearance daily: in the morning at the shambles, and at the market of St. Salvador; on fast-days at the fish-market; every afternoon on the quay, and on Thursdays at the fair.

All these lessons the two friends carefully stored in their memory, and the following morning both repaired in good time to the market of St. Salvador. Scarcely had they arrived before they were remarked by numbers of young fellows of the trade, who soon perceived, by the shining brightness of their bags and baskets, that they were new beginners. They were assailed with a thousand questions, to all of which they replied with great presence of mind and discretion. Presently up came two customers, one of whom had the appearance of a student; the other was a soldier. Both were attracted by the clean and new appearance of their baskets; and he who seemed to be a student beckoned Cortado, while the soldier engaged Rincon.

"In God's name be it!" exclaimed both the novices in a breath—Rincon adding, "It is a good beginning of the trade, master, since it is your Worship that is giving me my handsel."

"The handsel shall not be a bad one," replied the soldier, "seeing that I have been lucky at cards of late, and am in love. I propose this day to regale the friends of my lady with a feast, and am come to buy the materials."

"Load away, then, your Worship," replied Rincon, "and lay on me as much as you please, for I feel courage enough to carry off the whole market; nay, if you should desire me to aid in cooking what I carry, it shall be done with all my heart."

The soldier was pleased with the boy's ready good-will, and told him that if he felt disposed to enter his service he would relieve him from the degrading office he then bore. But Rincon declared that, since this was the first day on which he had tried it, he was not willing to abandon the work so soon, or at least until he had seen what profit there was to be made of it; but if it did not suit him, he gave the gentleman his word that he would prefer the service offered him even to that of a canon.

The soldier laughed, loaded him well, and showed him the house of his lady, bidding him observe it well that he might know it another time, so that he might be able to send him there again without being obliged to accompany him. Rincon promised fidelity and good conduct. The soldier gave him some small coins, and the lad returned like a shot to the market, that he might lose no opportunity by delay. Besides, he had been well advised in respect of diligence by the Asturian, who had likewise told him that when he was employed to carry small fish, such as sprats, sardines, or flounders, he might very well take a few for himself and have the first taste of them, were it only to diminish his expenses of the day, but that he must do this with infinite caution and prudence, lest the confidence of the employers should be disturbed; for to maintain confidence was above all things important in their trade.

But whatever haste Rincon had made to return, he found Cortado at his post before him. The latter instantly inquired how he had got on. Rincon opened his hand and showed his money, when Cortado, thrusting his arm into his bosom, drew forth a little purse which appeared to have once been of amber-colored silk, and was not badly filled. "It was with this," said he, "that my service to his reverence the student has been rewarded—with this and two quartos besides. Do you take it, Rincon, for fear of what may follow."

Cortado had scarcely given the purse in secret to his companion, before the student returned in a great heat and looking in mortal alarm. He no sooner set eyes on Cortado, than, hastening toward him, he inquired if he had by chance seen a purse with such and such marks and tokens, and which had disappeared, together with fifteen crowns in gold pieces, three double reals, and a certain number of maravedis in quartos and octavos. "Did you take it from me yourself," he added, "while I was buying in the market, with you standing beside me?"

To this Cortado replied with perfect composure, "All I can tell you of your purse is, that it cannot be lost, unless, indeed, your Worship has left it in bad hands."

"That is the very thing, sinner that I am," returned the student. "To a certainty I must have left it in bad hands, since it has been stolen from me."

"I say the same," rejoined Cortado; "but there is a remedy for every misfortune excepting death. The best thing your Worship can do now is to have patience, for after all it is God who has made us, and after one day there comes another. If one hour gives us wealth, another takes it away; but it may happen that the man who has stolen your purse may in time repent, and may return it to your Worship, with all the interest due on the loan."

"The interest I will forgive him," exclaimed the student. Cortado resumed, "There are, besides, those letters of excommunication; and there is also good diligence in seeking for the thief, which is the mother of success. Of a truth, sir, I would not willingly be in the place of him who has stolen your purse; for if your Worship have received any of the sacred orders, I should feel as if I had been guilty of some great crime—nay, of sacrilege—in stealing from your person."

"Most certainly the thief has committed a sacrilege," replied the student, in pitiable tones; "for although I am not in orders, but am only a sacristan of certain nuns, yet the money in my purse was the third of the income due from a chapelry, which I had been commissioned to receive by a priest, who is one of my friends, so that the purse does, in fact, contain blessed and sacred money."

"Let him eat his sin with his bread!" exclaimed Rincon at that moment. "I should be sorry to become bail for the profit he will obtain from it. There will be a day of judgment at the last, when all things will have to pass, as they say, through the holes of the colander, and it will then be known who was the scoundrel that has had the audacity to plunder and make off with the whole third of the revenue of a chapelry. But tell me, Mr. Sacristan, on your life, what is the amount of the whole yearly income?"

"Income to the devil, and you with it!" replied the sacristan, with more rage than was becoming. "Am I in the humor to talk to you about income? Tell me, brother, if you know anything of the purse; if not, God be with you. I must go and have it cried out."

"That does not seem to me so bad a remedy," remarked Cortado. "But I warn your Worship not to forget the precise description of the purse, nor the exact sum that it contains; for if you commit the error of a single mite, the money will never be suffered to appear again while the world is a world, and that you may take for a prophecy."

"I am not afraid of committing any mistake in describing the purse," returned the sacristan, "for I remember it better than I do the ringing of my bells, and I shall not commit the error of an atom." Saying this, he drew a laced handkerchief from his pocket to wipe away the perspiration which rained down his face as from an alembic; but no sooner had

Cortado set eyes on the handkerchief than he marked it for his own.

When the sacristan had got to a certain distance, therefore, Cortado followed, and having overtaken him as he was mounting the steps of a church, he took him apart, and poured forth so interminable a string of rigmarole, all about the theft of the purse, and the prospect of recovering it, that the poor sacristan could do nothing but listen with open mouth, unable to make head or tail of what he said, although he made him repeat it two or three times.

Cortado meanwhile continued to look fixedly into the eyes of the sacristan, whose own were riveted on the face of the boy, and seemed to hang, as it were, on his words. This gave Cortado an opportunity to finish his job, and having cleverly whipped the handkerchief out of the pocket, he took leave of the sacristan.—" *Exemplary Tales.*"

Doctor Glass-Case

Six months did Rodaja remain confined to his bed; and during that time he not only became reduced to a skeleton, but seemed also to have lost the use of his faculties. Every remedy that could be thought of was tried in his behalf. But although the physicians succeeded in curing the physical malady, they could not remove that of the mind; so that when he was at last pronounced cured, he was still afflicted with the strangest madness that was ever heard of among the many kinds by which humanity has been assailed. The unhappy man imagined that he was entirely made of glass; and, possessed with this idea, when any one approached him

he would utter the most terrible outcries, begging and beseeching them not to come near him, or they would assuredly
break him to pieces, as he was not like other men, but entirely of glass from head to foot.

In the hope of rousing him from this strange hallucination,
many persons, without regard to his prayers and cries, threw
themselves upon him and embraced him, bidding him observe
that he was not broken for all that. But all they gained by
this was to see the poor creature sink to the earth, uttering
lamentable moans, and instantly fall into a fainting fit, from
which he could not be recovered for several hours; nay,
when he did recover, it was but to renew his complaints,
from which he never desisted but to implore that such a
misfortune might not be suffered to happen again.

He exhorted every one to speak to him from a great distance, declaring that on this condition they might ask him
what they pleased, and that he could reply with all the more
effect, now he was a man of glass and not of flesh and bones;
since glass, being a substance of more delicate subtlety, per-
mits the soul to act with more promptitude and efficacy than
it can be expected to do in the heavier body formed of mere
earth.

Certain persons then desiring to ascertain if what he had
said were true, asked him many questions of great difficulty
respecting various circumstances; to all these he replied with
the utmost acuteness, insomuch that his answers awakened
astonishment in the most learned professors of medicine and
philosophy whom that university could boast. And well they
might be amazed at seeing a man who was subject to so
strange an hallucination as that of believing himself to be
made of glass, still retain such extraordinary judgment on
other points as to be capable of answering difficult questions

with the marvelous propriety and truth which distinguished the replies of Rodaja.

The poor man had often entreated that some case might be given to him wherein he might enclose the brittle vase of his body, so that he might not break it in putting on ordinary clothing. He was consequently furnished with a surplice of ample width, and a cloth wrapper, which he folded around him with much care, confining it to his waist with a girdle of soft cotton; but he would not wear any kind of shoes. The method he adopted to prevent any one from approaching him when they brought him food, was to fix an earthen pot into the cleft of a stick prepared for that purpose, and in this vessel he would receive such fruits as the season presented. He would not eat flesh or fish, nor would he drink anything but the water of the river, which he lapped from his hands.

In passing through the streets, Rodaja was in the habit of walking carefully in the middle of them, lest a tile should fall from the houses upon his head and break it. In the summer he slept in the open air, and in the winter he lodged at one of the inns, where he buried himself in straw to his throat, remarking that this was the most proper and secure bed for men of glass. When it thundered, Rodaja trembled like an aspen leaf, and would rush out into the fields, not returning to the city until the storm had passed.

His friends kept him shut up for some time, but perceiving that his malady increased, they at last complied with his earnest request that they would let him go about freely; and he might be seen walking through the streets of the city, dressed as we have described, to the astonishment and regret of all who knew him.

The boys soon got about him, but he kept them off with

his staff, requesting them to speak to him from a distance,
lest they should break him, seeing that he, being a man of
glass, was exceedingly tender and brittle. But far from
listening to his request, the boys, who are the most perverse
generation in the world, soon began to throw various missiles
and even stones at him, notwithstanding all his prayers and
exclamations. They declared that they wished to see if he
were in truth of glass, as he affirmed; but the lamentations
and outcries of the poor maniac induced the grown persons
who were near to reprove and even beat the boys, whom
they drove away for the moment, but who did not fail to
return at the next opportunity.

One day, when a horde of these tormentors had pursued
him with more than their usual pertinacity, and had worn
out his patience, he turned to them, saying, " What do you
want with me, you varlets, more obstinate than flies, more
disgusting than bugs, and bolder than the boldest fleas? Am
I, perchance, the Monte Testacio of Rome, that you cast
upon me so many potsherds and tiles?"

But Rodaja was followed by many who kept about him for
the purpose of hearing him reply to the questions asked, or
reprove the questioner, as the case might be. And after a
time even the boys found it more amusing to listen to his
words than to throw tiles at him, when they gave him, for
the most part, somewhat less annoyance.

The maniac Rodaja was one day passing through the
ropery at Salamanca, when a woman who was working
there accosted him, and said, " By my soul, Sir Doctor, I am
sorry for your misfortune, but what shall I do for you, since,
try as I may, I cannot weep?"

To which Rodaja, fixedly regarding her, gravely replied,
"*Filiæ Jerusalem, plorate super vos et super filios vestros.*"

The husband of the rope-worker was standing by, and, comprehending the reply, he said to Rodaja, "Brother Glass-case—for so they tell me you are to be called—you have more of the rogue than the fool in you!"

"You are not called on to give me an obolus," rejoined Rodaja, "for I have not a grain of the fool about me!"

One day when he was passing near a house well known as the resort of thieves and other disorderly persons, he saw several of the inhabitants assembled round the door, and called out, "See, here you have baggage belonging to the army of Satan, and it is lodged in the house of hell accordingly."

A man once asked him what advice he should give to a friend whose wife had left him for another, and who was in great sorrow for her loss. "You shall bid him thank God," replied Rodaja, "for the favor he has obtained, in that his enemy is removed from his house."

"Then you would not have him go seek her?" inquired the other.

"Let him not even think of doing so," returned Rodaja, "for if he find her, what will he have gained but the perpetual evidence of his dishonor?"

"And what shall I do to keep peace with my own wife?" inquired the same person.

"Give her all that she can need or rightfully claim," said the maniac, "and let her be mistress of every person and thing thy house contains, but take care that she be not mistress of thyself."

A boy one day said to him, "Master Glass-case, I have a mind to run away from my father, and leave my home forever, because he beats me."

"I would have thee beware, boy," replied Rodaja. "The stripes given by a father are no dishonor to the son, and may save him from those of the hangman, which are indeed a disgrace."

Intelligence of his peculiar state, with a description of the replies he gave and the remarks he uttered, was much spread abroad, more especially among those who had known him in different parts, and great sorrow was expressed for the loss of a man who had given so fair a promise of distinction. A person of high rank then at court wrote to a friend of his at Salamanca, begging that Rodaja might be sent to him at Valladolid, and charging his friend to make all needful arrangements for that purpose. The gentleman consequently accosted Vidriera the next time he met him, and said, "Dr. Glass-case, you are to know that a great noble of the court is anxious to have you go to Valladolid."

Whereupon Rodaja replied, "Your Worship will excuse me to that nobleman, and say that I am not fit to dwell at court, nor in the palace, because I have some sense of shame left, and do not know how to flatter."

He was nevertheless persuaded to go, and the mode in which he traveled was as follows: a large pannier of that kind in which glass is transported was prepared, and in this Rodaja was placed, well defended by straw, which was brought up to his neck, the opposite pannier being carefully balanced by means of stones, among which appeared the necks of bottles, since Rodaja desired it to be understood that he was sent as a vessel of glass. In this fashion he journeyed to Valladolid, which city he entered by night, and was not unpacked until he had first been carefully deposited in the house of the noble who had requested his presence.

By this gentleman he was received with much kindness, and the latter said to him, "You are extremely welcome, Dr. Glass-case. I hope you have had a pleasant journey."

Rodaja replied that no journey could be called a bad one if it took you safe to your end, unless, indeed, it were that which led to the gallows.

Being one day shown the falconry, wherein were numerous falcons and other birds of similar kind, he remarked that the sport pursued by means of those birds was entirely suitable to great nobles, since the cost was as two thousand to one of the profit.

When it pleased Rodaja to go forth into the city, the nobleman caused him to be attended by a servant, whose office it was to protect him from intrusion, and see that he was not molested by the boys of the place, by whom he was at once remarked. Indeed, but few days elapsed before he became known to the whole city, since he never failed to find a reply for all who questioned or consulted him.

Among those of the former class, there once came a student, who inquired if he were a poet; to which Rodaja replied, that up to the moment they had then arrived at he had neither been so stupid nor so bold as to become a poet. "I do not understand what you mean by so stupid or so bold, Dr. Glass-case," rejoined the student. To which Rodaja made answer, "I am not so stupid as to be a bad poet, nor so bold as to think myself capable of being a good one."

The student then inquired in what estimation he held poets, to which he answered that he held the poets themselves in but little esteem; but as to their art, that he esteemed greatly. His hearer inquiring further what he meant by that, Rodaja said that among the innumerable poets, by courtesy so called, the number of good ones was so small as scarcely to count at all, and that as the bad were not true poets, he could not admire them; but that he admired and even reverenced greatly the art of poetry, which does in fact comprise every other in itself, since it avails itself of all things, and purifies and beautifies all things, bringing its own marvelous productions to light for the advantage, the delectation, and the wonder of the world, which it fills with its benefits. He added further, "I know thoroughly to what extent and for what qualities we ought to estimate the good poet, since I perfectly well remember certain verses of Ovid," which he proceeded to quote. He then went on:

"Who is there that has not seen a wretched scribbler longing to bring some sonnet to the ears of his neighbors? How he goes round and round them, with ' Will your Worships excuse me if I read you a little sonnet, which I made one night on a certain occasion? for it appears to me, although indeed it be worth nothing, to have yet a certain something that I might call pretty and pleasing.' Then shall he twist his lips, and arch his eyebrows, and make a thousand antics, diving into his pockets meanwhile and bringing out half a hundred scraps of paper, greasy and torn, as if he had made a good million of sonnets. He then recites that which he proffered to the company, reading it in a chanting and affected voice. If, perchance, those who hear him, whether because of their knowledge or their ignorance, should fail to commend him, he says, 'Either your Worships have not listened to the verses, or I have not been able to read them properly, for in deed and in truth they deserve to be heard.' And he begins, as before, to recite his poem, with new gestures and varied pauses. . . ."

Rodaja was once asked how it happened that poets were always poor, to which he replied:

"If they were poor, it was because they chose to be so, since it was always in their power to be rich, if they would only take advantage of the opportunities in their hands,

For see how rich are their ladies!" he added. "Have they not all a very profusion of wealth in their possession? Is not their hair of gold? Are not their brows of burnished silver, their eyes of the most precious jewels, their lips of coral, their throats of ivory and transparent crystal? Are not their tears liquid pearls, and where they plant the soles of their feet do not jasmine and roses spring up at the moment, however rebellious and sterile the earth may previously have been? Then what is their breath but pure amber, musk, and frankincense? Yet to whom do all these things belong, if not to the poets? They are, therefore, manifest signs and proofs of their great riches."

In this manner he always spoke of bad poets. As to the good ones, he was loud in their praise, and exalted them above the horns of the moon.

Being at San Francisco, he one day saw some very indifferent pictures, by an incapable hand; whereupon he remarked that the good painters imitate Nature, while the bad ones have the impertinence to daub her face.

Having planted himself one day in front of a bookseller's shop with great care, to avoid being broken, he began to talk to the owner, and said, "This trade would please me greatly were it not for one fault that it has."

The bookseller inquiring what that might be, Rodaja replied, "It is the tricks you play on the writers when you purchase the copyright of a book, and the sport you make of the author if, perchance, he desire to print at his own cost. For what is your method of proceeding? Instead of the one thousand five hundred copies which you agree to print for him, you print three thousand; and when the author supposes that you are selling his books, you are but disposing of your own."

Miguel Cervantes

One of those men who carry sedan-chairs, once standing by while Rodaja was enumerating the faults committed by various trades and occupations, remarked to the latter, " Of us, Sir Doctor, you can find nothing amiss to say."

" Nothing," replied Rodaja, " except that you are made acquainted with more sins than are known to the confessor; but with this difference, that the confessor learns them to keep all secret, but you to make them the public talk of the taverns."

A muleteer who heard this—for all kinds of people were continually listening to him—said aloud, " There is little or nothing that you can say of us, Sir Phial, for we are people of great worth, and very useful servants to the commonwealth."

To which the man of glass replied, " The honor of the master exalts the honor of the servant. You, therefore, who call those who hire your mules your masters, see whom you serve, and what honor you may borrow from them; for your employers are some of the dirtiest rubbish that this earth endures.

" Once, when I was not a man of glass, I was traveling on a mule which I had hired, and I counted in her master one hundred and twenty-one defects, all capital ones, and all enemies to the human kind. All muleteers have a touch of the ruffian, a spice of the thief, and a dash of the mountebank. If their masters, as they call those they take on their mules, be of the butter-mouthed kind, they play more pranks with them than all the rogues of this city could perform in a year. If they be strangers, the muleteers rob them; if students, they malign them; if monks, they blaspheme them; but if soldiers, they tremble before them. These men, with the sailors, the carters, and the pack-carriers, lead a sort of life which is truly singular, and belongs to themselves alone.

"The carter passes the greater part of his days in a space not more than a yard and a half long, for there cannot be much more between the yoke of his mules and the mouth of his cart. He is singing for one-half of his time, and blaspheming the other; and if he have to drag one of his wheels out of a hole in the mire, he is more aided, as it might seem, by two great oaths than by three strong mules.

"The mariners are a pleasant people, but very unlike those of the towns, and they can speak no other language than that used in ships. When the weather is fine they are very diligent, but very idle when it is stormy. During a tempest they order much and obey little. Their ship, which is their mess-room, is also their god, and their pastime is the torment endured by seasick passengers.

"As to the muleteers, they are a race which has taken out a divorce from all sheets, and has married the pack-saddle. So diligent and careful are these excellent men, that to save themselves from losing a day they will lose their souls. Their music is the tramp of a hoof; their sauce is hunger; their matins are an exchange of abuse and bad words; their Mass is—to hear none at all."

While speaking thus, Rodaja stood at an apothecary's door, and, turning to the master of the shop, he said, "Your Worship's occupation would be a most salutary one if it were not so great an enemy to your lamps."

"Wherein is my trade an enemy to my lamps?" asked the apothecary.

"In this way," replied Rodaja: "whenever other oils fail you, immediately you take that of the lamp, as being the one which most readily comes to hand. But there is, indeed, another fault in your trade, and one that would suffice to ruin the best accredited physician in the world."

Being asked what that was, he replied that an apothecary never ventured to confess, or would admit, that any drug was absent from his stock; and so, if he have not the medicine prescribed, he makes use of some other which, in his opinion, has the same virtues and qualities; but as that is very seldom the case, the medicine, being badly compounded, produces an effect contrary to that expected by the physician.

Rodaja was then asked what he thought of the physicians themselves, and he replied as follows:

" The judge may distort or delay the justice which he should render us; the lawyer may support an unjust demand; the merchant may help us to squander our estate, and, in a word, all those with whom we have to deal in common life may do us more or less injury; but to kill us without fear, and standing quietly at his ease, unsheathing no other sword than that wrapped in the folds of a recipe, and without being subject to any danger of punishment, that can be done only by the physician; he alone can escape all fear of the discovery of his crimes, because at the moment of committing them he puts them under the earth. When I was a man of flesh, and not of glass, as I now am, I saw many things that might be adduced in support of what I have now said, but the relation of these I defer to some other time."

A certain person asked him what he should do to avoid envying another, and Rodaja bade him go to sleep—" For," said he, " while you sleep you will be the equal of him whom you envy."

It happened on another occasion that the criminal judge passed before the place where Rodaja stood. There was a great crowd of people, and two constables attended the magistrate, who was proceeding to his court, when Rodaja inquired his name. Being told, he replied:

"Now, I would lay a wager that this judge has vipers in his bosom, pistols in his inkhorn, and flashes of lightning in his hands, to destroy all that shall come within his commission. I once had a friend who inflicted so exorbitant a sentence in respect to a criminal commission which he held, that it exceeded by many carats the amount of guilt incurred by the crime of the delinquents. I inquired of him wherefore he had uttered so cruel a sentence and committed so manifest an injustice. To which he answered that he intended to grant permission of appeal, and that in this way he left the field open for the lords of the council to show their mercy by moderating and reducing that too rigorous punishment to its due proportions. But I told him it would have been still better for him to have given such a sentence as would have rendered their labor unnecessary, by which means he would also have merited and obtained the reputation of being a wise and exact judge."

Among the number of those by whom Rodaja was constantly surrounded was an acquaintance of his own, who permitted himself to be saluted as the Doctor, although Rodaja knew well that he had not taken even the degree of bachelor. To him, therefore, he one day said:

"Take care, gossip mine, that you and your title do not meet with the Fathers of the Redemption, for they will certainly take possession of your doctorship as being a creature unrighteously detained captive."

"Let us behave well to each other, Dr. Glass-case," said the other, "since you know that I am a man of high and profound learning."

"I know you rather to be a Tantalus in the same," replied

Rodaja; "for if learning reach high to you, you are never able to plunge into its depths."

He was one day leaning against the stall of a tailor, who was seated with his hands before him, and to whom he said, "Without doubt, you are in the way to salvation."

"From what symptom do you judge me to be so, Sir Doctor?" inquired the tailor.

"From the fact that, as you have nothing to do, so you have nothing to lie about, and may cease lying, which is a great step."

Of the shoemakers he said that not one of that trade ever performed his office badly; seeing that if the shoe be too narrow, and pinches the foot, the shoemaker says, "In two hours it will be as wide as a cord sandal"; or he declares it right that it should be narrow, since the shoe of a gentleman must needs fit closely; and if it be too wide, he maintains that it still ought to be so, for the ease of the foot, and lest a man should have the gout.

Seeing the waiting-maid of an actress attending her mistress, he said she was much to be pitied who had to serve so many women, to say nothing of the men whom she also had to wait on. The bystanders requiring to know how the damsel, who had but to serve one, could be said to wait on so many, he replied, "Is she not the waiting-maid of a queen, a nymph, a goddess, a scullery-maid, and a shepherdess? Besides that, she is also the servant of a page and a lackey. For all these, and many more, are in the person of an actress."

Some one asked Rodaja who had been the happiest man in the world. To which he answered, "Nobody; because nobody knows who his father is, nobody lives blameless, nobody is satisfied with his lot, and nobody goes to heaven."

Of the fencing-masters he said that they were professors of an art which was never to be known when it was most wanted, since they pretended to reduce to mathematical demonstrations, which are infallible, the angry thoughts and movements of a man's adversaries.

To such men as dyed their beards Rodaja always exhibited a particular enmity. One day, observing a Portuguese, whose beard he knew to be dyed, in dispute with a Spaniard, to whom he said, " I swear by the beard that I wear on my face," Rodaja called out to him, " Halt there, friend! You should not say that you *wear* on your face, but that you dye on your face."

To another, whose beard had been streaked by an imperfect dye, Dr. Glass-case said, " Your beard is true dust-colored piebald."

He related, on another occasion, that a certain damsel, discreetly conforming to the will of her parents, had agreed to marry an old man with a white beard, who, on the evening before his marriage was to take place, thought fit to have his beard dyed, and whereas he had taken it from the sight of his betrothed as white as snow, he presented it at the altar with a color blacker than that of pitch. Seeing this, the damsel turned to her parents and requested them to give her the spouse they had promised, saying that she would have him, and no other. They assured her that he whom she there saw was the person they had before shown her, and given her for her spouse; but she refused to believe it, maintaining that he whom her parents had given her was a grave person, with a white beard. Nor was she by any means to be persuaded that the dyed man before her was her betrothed, and the marriage was broken off.

Toward elderly ladies' companions he entertained as great

a dislike as toward those who dyed their beards; uttering wonderful things respecting their falsehood and affectation, their tricks and pretenses, their simulated scruples and their real wickedness; reproaching them with their fancied maladies of stomach, and the frequent giddiness with which they were afflicted in the head. Nay, even their mode of speaking was made the subject of his censure; and he declared that there were more turns in their speech than folds in their great togas and wide gowns. Finally, he declared them altogether useless, if not much worse.

Being one day much tormented by a hornet which settled on his neck, he nevertheless refused to take it off, lest in seeking to catch the insect he should break himself; but he still complained wofully of the sting. Some one then remarked to him that it was scarcely to be supposed he would feel it much, since his whole person was of glass. But Rodaja replied that the hornet in question must needs be a slanderer, seeing that slanderers were of a race whose tongues were capable of penetrating bodies of bronze, to say nothing of glass.

A monk who was enormously fat one day passed near where Rodaja was sitting, when one who stood by ironically remarked that the father was so reduced and consumptive as scarcely to be capable of walking. Offended by this, Rodaja exclaimed, "Let none forget the words of holy Scripture, *'Nolite tangere Christos meos'*"; and, becoming still more heated, he bade those around him reflect a little, when they would see that, of the many saints canonized and placed among the number of the blessed by the Church within a few years in those parts, none had been called Captain Don Such a One, or Lawyer Don So-and-So, or Marquis of Such a Place; but all were Brother Diego, Brother Jacinto, or

Brother Raimundo, all monks and friars, proceeding, that is to say, from the monastic orders. "These," he added, "are the orange-trees of heaven, whose fruits are placed on the table of God."

Of evil-speakers Rodaja said that they were like the feathers of the eagle, which gnaw, wear away, and reduce to nothing, whatever feathers of other birds are mingled with them in beds or cushions, how good soever those feathers may be.

Concerning the keepers of gaming-houses he uttered wonders, and many more than can here be repeated—commending highly the patience of a certain gamester, who would remain all night playing and losing. Yea, though of choleric disposition by nature, he would never open his mouth to complain, although he was suffering the martyrdom of Barabbas, provided only his adversary did not cut the cards. In a word, Rodaja uttered so many sage remarks that, had it not been for the cries he sent forth when any one approached near enough to touch him, and for his peculiar dress, slight food, strange manner of eating, sleeping in the air, or lying buried in straw, no one would have supposed but that he was one of the most acute persons in the world.

—"Exemplary Tales."

Tome Burguillos

To-Morrow

I DREAM of a to-morrow, which to-morrow
  Will be as distant then as 'tis to-day;
For Phœbus, who oft teases man with sorrow,
  Will never turn his car to light my way.
 So that I'm certain now *that* morning's ray
Will never dawn; and, Phyllis, thou mayst borrow
Some other phrase from language for to-morrow,
  And to-morrow, and to-morrow—but betray.
I called upon Dan Cupid (when I find
  Sweet company I never walk alone),
And said, " Come with me, an you are inclined;
  Let's seek this maiden morrow, for I groan
Impatient." Then I curse my eyes—they're blind.
  Oh, no, I will not curse them—they're my own.

José Morell

Advice to an Innkeeper

"MINGLE the sweet and useful," says a sage,
Whose name, perchance, is lost in history's page,
But whose advice withal is good and wise.
It caught a tavern-keeper's busy eyes,
And he exclaimed, "Delightful! That's for me!
I see the sense, I read the mystery;
This is its meaning, I can well divine:
'Mix useful water with your luscious wine.'"

To a Poet

YOU say your verses are of gold.
  And how, my friend? I'd fain inquire.
But, no—I see the truth you've told:
  They must be purified by fire.

Calderon de la Barca

The Mayor of Zalamea—Act I

PEDRO CRESPO, *subsequently Mayor of Zalamea.*	DON ALVARO, *Captain.*
JUAN, *his Son.*	DON MENDO, *Nobleman.*
ISABEL, *his Daughter.*	NUNO, *his Servant.*
INES, *his Niece.*	A SERGEANT.
DON LOPE, *Commander.*	REBOLLEDO, *a Soldier.*
	CHISPA, *his Mistress.*

SCENE I. *Country near Zalamea.*

REBOLLEDO, CHISPA, *and* SOLDIERS.

Reb. Confound, say I, these forced marches from place to place, without halt or bait. What say you, friends?

All. Amen!

Reb. To be trailed over the country like a pack of gipsies, after a little scrap of flag upon a pole, eh?

1st Sold. Rebolledo's off!

Reb. And that infernal drum, which has at last been good enough to stop a moment stunning us.

2d Sold. Come, come, Rebolledo, don't storm; we shall soon be at Zalamea.

Reb. And where will be the good of that if I'm dead before I get there? And if not, 'twill only be from bad to worse: for if we all reach the place alive, as sure as death up comes Mr. Mayor to persuade the commissary we had better march on to the next town. At first Mr. Commissary replies very virtuously, "Impossible! The men are fagged to death." But after a little pocket persuasion, then it's all "Gentlemen, I'm very sorry; but orders have come for us to march forward, and immediately." And away we have to trot, foot-weary, dust-bedraggled, and starved as we are. Well, I swear if I do get alive to Zalamea to-day, I'll not leave it on this side o' sunrise for love, lash, or money. It won't be the first time in my life I've given 'em the slip.

1st Sold. Nor the first time a poor fellow has had the slip given him for doing so. And more likely than ever, now that Don Lope de Figuerroa has taken the command. A fine, brave fellow they say, but a devil of a Tartar, who'll have every inch of duty done, or take the change out of his own son, without waiting for trial either.

Reb. Listen to this now, gentlemen! By Heaven, I'll be beforehand with him!

2d Sold. Come, come, a soldier shouldn't talk so.

Reb. I tell you it isn't for myself I care so much, as for this poor little thing that follows me.

Chis. Master Rebolledo, don't you fret about me. You know I was born with a beard on my heart, if not on my chin, if ever girl was; and your fearing for me is as bad as if I were afraid myself. Why, when I came along with you I made up my mind to hardship and danger for honor's sake; else, if I'd wanted to live in clover, I never should have left the alderman who kept such a table as all aldermen don't, I promise you. Well, what's the odds? I chose to leave him and follow the drum, and here I am, and if I don't flinch, why should you?

Reb. 'Fore Heaven, you're the crown of womankind!

Solds. So she is! so she is! Long live Chispa!

Reb. And so she is, and one cheer more for her. Hurrah! Especially if she'll give us a song to lighten the way.

Chis. The castanet shall answer for me.

Reb. I'll join in; and do you, comrades, bear a hand in the chorus.

Solds. Fire away!

CHISPA *sings.*

"Titiri tiri, marching is weary;
　Weary, weary, and long is the way.
Titiri tiri, hither, my deary—
　What meat have you got for the soldier to-day?"
"Meat have I none, my merry men."
"Titiri tiri, then kill the old hen."
"Alas and a day! the old hen is dead!"
"Then give us a cake from the oven instead.
　Titiri titiri titiri tiri,
Give us a cake from the oven instead."

"Admiral, admiral, where have you been-a?"
　"I've been fighting where the waves roar."
"Ensign, ensign, what have you seen-a?"
　"Glory and honor and gunshot galore
Fighting the Moors in column and line.
Poor fellows, they never hurt me or mine—
　Titiri titiri titiri tina."

1st Sold. Look, look, comrades! What between singing and grumbling we never noticed yonder church among the trees.

Reb. Is that Zalamea?

Chis. Yes, that it is; I know the steeple. Hurrah! We'll

finish the song when we get into quarters, or have another
as good; for you know I have 'em of all sorts and sizes.

Reb. Stop a moment, here's the sergeant.

2d Sold. And the captain too.

Enter Don Alvaro *and* Sergeant.

Alv. Good news, gentlemen: no more marching, for to-
day at least. We halt at Zalamea till Don Lope joins with
the rest of the regiment from Llerena. So, who knows but
you may have several days' rest here?

Reb. and Solds. Huzzah for our captain!

Alv. Your quarters are ready, and the commissary will
give every one his billet on marching in.

Chis. (*singing*). Now, then, for

"Titiri tiri, hither, my deary—
Heat the oven and kill the old hen."

(*Exit, with* Soldiers.)

Alv. Well, Sergeant, have you my billet?

Serg. Yes, sir.

Alv. And where am I to put up?

Serg. With the richest man in Zalamea, a farmer, as
proud as Lucifer's heir-apparent.

Alv. Ah! the old story of an upstart.

Serg. However, sir, you have the best quarters in the
place, including his daughter, who is, they say, the prettiest
woman in Zalamea.

Alv. Pooh! a pretty peasant! Splay hands and feet!

Serg. Shame! Shame!

Alv. Isn't it true, puppy?

Alv. What would a man on march have better than a
pretty country lass to toy with?

Alv. Well, I never saw one I cared for, even on march I can't call a woman a woman unless she's clean about the hands and fetlocks, and otherwise well appointed—a lady, in short.

Serg. Well, any one for me who'll let me kiss her. Come, sir, let us be going, for if you won't be at her, I will.

Alv. Look, look, yonder!

Serg. Why, it must be Don Quixote himself, with his very Rosinante, too, that Cervantes writes of.

Alv. And his Sancho at his side. Well, do you carry my kit on before to quarters, and then come and tell me when all's ready.   (*Exeunt.*)

SCENE II. *Zalamea, before* CRESPO'S *House.*

DON MENDO *and* NUNO.

Men. How's the gray horse?

Nun. You may as well call him the dun; so screw'd he can't move a leg.

Men. Did you have him walked gently about?

Nun. Walked about? when it's corn he wants, poor devil?

Men. And the dogs?

Nun. Ah, now, they might do, if you'd give them the horse to eat.

Men. Enough, enough! it has struck three. My gloves and toothpick.

Nun. That sinecure toothpick!

Men. I tell you I would brain anybody who insinuated to me I had not dined—and on game too. But tell me, Nuño, haven't the soldiers come into Zalamea this afternoon?

Nun. Yes, sir.

Men. What a nuisance for the commonalty who have to quarter them!

Nun. But worse for those who haven't.

Men. What do you mean, sir?

Nun. I mean the squires. Ah, sir, if the soldiers aren't billeted on them, do you know why?

Men. Well, why?

Nun. For fear of being starved—which would be a bad job for the king's service.

Men. God rest my father's soul, says I, who left me a pedigree and patent all blazoned in gold and azure, that exempts me from such impositions!

Nun. I wish he'd left you the gold in a more available shape, however.

Men. Though, indeed, when I come to think of it, I don't know if I owe him any thanks; considering that unless he had consented to beget me a nobleman at once, I wouldn't have been born at all, for him or any one.

Nun. Humph! Could you have helped it?

Men. Easily.

Nun. How, sir?

Men. You must know that every one that is born is the essence of the food his parents eat.

Nun. Oh! Your parents did eat, then, sir? You have not inherited *that* of them, at all events.

Men. Which forthwith converts itself into proper flesh and blood; *ergo,* if my father had been an eater of onions, for instance, he would have begotten me with a strong breath; on which I should have said to him, "Hold! I must come of no such nastiness as that, I promise you."

Nun. Ah! now I see the old saying is true.

Men. What is that?

Nun. That hunger sharpens wit.

Men. Knave, do you insinuate——

Nun. I only know it is now three o'clock, and we have neither of us yet had anything but our own spittle to chew.

Men. Perhaps so, but there are distinctions of rank. A nobleman, sir, has no belly.

Nun. Oh, Lord! that I were a nobleman!

Men. Possibly. Servants must learn moderation in all things. But let me hear no more of the matter; we are under Isabel's window.

Nun. There again: if you are so devoted an admirer, why on earth, sir, don't you ask her in marriage of her father? By doing so you would kill two birds with one stone: get yourself something to eat, and his grandchildren squires.

Men. Hold your tongue, sir! it is impious. Am I, a nobleman with such a pedigree, to demean myself with a plebeian connection just for money's sake?

Nun. Well, I've always heard say a mean father-in-law is best. Better stumble on a pebble than run your head against a post. But, however, if you don't mean marriage, sir, what do you mean?

Men. And pray, sir, can't I dispose of her in a convent in case I get tired of her? But go directly, and tell me if you can get a sight of her.

Nun. I'm afraid lest her father should get a sight of me.

Men. And what if he do, being my man? Go and do as I bid you.

Nun. (*after going to look*). Come, sir, you owe one meal at least now. She's at the window, with her cousin.

Men. Go again, and tell her something about her window being another East, and she a second Sun dawning from it in the afternoon.

(ISABEL *and* INES *come to the window.*)

Ines. For Heaven's sake, cousin, let's stand here and see the soldiers march in.

Isab. Not I, while that man is in the way, Ines. You know how I hate the sight of him.

Ines. With all his devotion to you?

Isab. I wish he would spare himself and me the trouble.

Ines. I think you are wrong to take it as an affront.

Isab. How would you have me take it?

Ines. Why, as a compliment.

Isab. What, when I hate the man?

Men. Ah! 'pon the honor of a nobleman, which is a sacred oath, I could have sworn that till this moment the sun had not risen. But why should I wonder, when, indeed, a second Aurora——

Isab. Don Mendo, how often have I told you not to waste your time playing these fool's antics before my window day after day?

Men. If a pretty woman only knew how anger improved her beauty! Her complexion needs no other paint than indignation. Go on, go on, lovely one, grow angrier, and lovelier still!

Isab. You sha'n't have even that consolation. Come, Ines. (*Exit.*)

Ines. Beware of the portcullis, sir knight.

(*Shuts down the blind in his face.*)

Men. Ines, beauty must be ever victorious, whether advancing or in retreat.

Calderon de la Barca

Enter CRESPO.

Cres. That I can never go in or out of my house without that squireen haunting it!

Nun. Pedro Crespo, sir!

Men. Oh! Ah! Let us turn another way. 'Tis an ill-conditioned fellow.

As he turns, enter JUAN.

Juan. That I never can come home but this ghost of a Mendo is there to spoil my appetite.

Nun. His son, sir!

Men. He's worse. (*Turning back.*) Oh, Pedro Crespo, good day. Crespo, good man, good day.

(*Exit with* NUNO.)

Cres. Good day, indeed! I'll make it bad day one of these days with you, if you don't take care. But how now, Juanito, my boy?

Juan. I was looking for you, sir, but could not find you. Where have you been?

Cres.
To the barn, where high and dry
The jolly sheaves of corn do lie,
Which the sun, arch-chemist old,
Turn'd from black earth into gold,
And the swinging flail one day
On the barn-floor shall assay,
Separating the pure ore
From the drossy chaff away.
This I've been about. And now,
Juanito, what hast thou?

207

Juan. Alas, sir, I can't answer in so good rime or reason. I have been playing at fives, and lost every bout.

Cres. What signifies if you paid?

Juan. But I could not, and have come to you for the money.

Cres.
Before I give it you, listen to me:
There are things two
Thou never must do:
Swear to more than thou knowest,
Play for more than thou owest;
And never mind cost,
So credit's not lost.

Juan. Good advice, sir, no doubt, that I shall lay by for its own sake as well as for yours. Meanwhile, I have also heard say:

Preach not to a beggar till
The beggar's empty hide you fill.

Cres. 'Fore Heaven, thou pay'st me in my own coin. But——

Enter SERGEANT.

Serg. Pray, does one Pedro Crespo live hereabout?

Cres. Have you any commands for him if he does?

Serg. Yes, to tell him of the arrival of Don Alvaro de 'Ataide, captain of the troop that has just marched into Zalamea, and quartered upon him.

Cres. Say no more. My house and all I have is ever at the service of the king, and of all who have authority under him. If you leave his things here, I will see his room is got ready directly; and do you tell his Honor that, come when he will, he shall find me and mine at his service.

Serg. Good! He will be here directly. (*Exit.*)

Juan. I wonder, father, that, rich as you are, you still submit yourself to these nuisances.

Cres. Why, boy, how could I help them?

Juan. You know: by buying a patent of gentility.

Cres. A patent of gentility! Upon thy life, now, dost think there's a soul who doesn't know that I'm no gentleman at all, but just a plain farmer? What's the use of my buying a patent of gentility, if I can't buy the gentle blood along with it? Will any one think me a bit more of a gentleman for buying fifty patents? Not a whit! I should only prove I was worth so many thousand royals, not that I had gentle blood in my veins, which can't be bought at any price. If a fellow's been bald ever so long, and buys him a fine wig and claps it on, will his neighbors think it is his own hair a bit the more? No; they will say, " So-and-So has a fine wig, and, what's more, he must have paid handsomely for it too." But they know his bald pate is safe under it all the while. That's all he gets by it.

Juan. Nay, sir, he gets to look younger and handsomer, and keeps off sun and cold.

Cres. Tut! I'll have none of your wig honor at any price. My grandfather was a farmer, so was my father, so is yours, and so shall you be after him. Go, call your sister.

Enter ISABEL *and* INES.

Oh, here she is. Daughter, our gracious king—whose life God save these thousand years!—is on his way to be crowned at Lisbon. Thither the troops are marching from all quarters, and among others that fine veteran Flanders regiment, commanded by the famous Don Lope de Figuerroa, will march into Zalamea, and be quartered here to-day—some of the soldiers in my house. Is it not as well you should be out of the way?

Isab. Sir, 'twas upon this very errand I came to you, knowing what nonsense I shall have to hear if I stay below. My cousin and I can go up to the garret, and there keep so close, the very sun shall not know of our whereabout.

Cres. That's my good girl. Juanito, you wait here to receive them in case they come while I am out looking after their entertainment.

Isab. Come, Ines.

Ines. Very well——

> Though I've heard in a song what folly 'twould be
> To try keep in a loft what won't keep on the tree.

(Exeunt.)

Enter Don Alvaro *and* Sergeant.

Serg. This is the house, sir.

Alv. Is my kit come?

Serg. Yes, sir, and (*aside*) I'll be the first to take an inventory of the pretty daughter. (*Exit.*)

Juan. Welcome, sir, to our house. We count it a great honor to have such a cavalier as yourself for a guest, I assure you. (*Aside.*) What a fine fellow! What an air! I long to try the uniform, somehow.

Alv. Thank you, my lad.

Juan. You must forgive our poor house, which we devoutly wish was a palace for your sake. My father is gone

after your supper, sir. May I go and see that your chamber
is got ready for you?

Alv. Thank you! thank you!

Juan. Your servant, sir. (*Exit.*)

Enter SERGEANT.

Alv. Well, sergeant, where's the Dulcinea you told me of?

Serg. Deuce take me, sir, if I haven't been looking everywhere, in parlor, bedroom, kitchen, and scullery, up-stairs
and down-stairs, and can't find her out.

Alv. Oh, no doubt the old fellow has hid her away for
fear of us.

Serg. Yes, I asked a serving-wench, and she confessed
her master had locked the girl up in the attic, with strict
orders not even to look out so long as we were in the place.

Alv. Ah! these clodpoles are all so jealous of the service.
And what is the upshot? Why, I, who didn't care a pin to
see her before, shall never rest till I get at her now.

Serg. But how, without a blow-up?

Alv. Let me see—how shall we manage it?

Serg. The more difficult the enterprise, the more glory in
success, you know, in love as in war.

Alv. I have it!

Serg. Well, sir?

Alv. You shall pretend— But no, here comes one will
serve my turn better.

Enter REBOLLEDO *and* CHISPA.

Reb. (*to* CHISPA). There he is. Now, if I can get him
into a good humor——

Chis. Speak up, then, like a man.

Reb. I wish I'd some of your courage. But don't you leave me while I tackle him. Please your Honor——

Alv. (*to* SERGEANT). I tell you I've my eye on Rebolledo to do him a good turn. I like his spirit.

Serg. Ah, he's one of a thousand.

Reb. (*aside*). Here's luck! Please your Honor——

Alv. Oh, Rebolledo. Well, Rebolledo, what is it?

Reb. You may know I am a gentleman who has, by ill luck, lost all his estate—all that ever I had, have, shall have, may have, or can have, through all the conjugation of the verb "to have." And I want your Honor——

Alv. Well?

Reb. To desire the ensign to appoint me roulette-master to the regiment, so I may pay my liabilities like a man of honor.

Alv. Quite right! Quite right! I will see it done.

Chis. Oh, brave captain! Oh, if I only live to hear them all call me Madam Roulette!

Reb. Shall I go at once and tell him?

Alv. Wait. I want you first to help me in a little plan I have.

Reb. Out with it, noble captain! Slow said slow sped, you know.

Alv. You are a good fellow. Listen: I want to get into that attic there, for a particular purpose.

Reb. And why doesn't your Honor go up at once?

Alv. I don't like to do it in a strange house without an excuse. Now look here: you and I will pretend to quarrel; I get angry and draw my sword, and you run away up-stairs, and I after you, to the attic; that's all. I'll manage the rest.

Chis. Ah, we get on famously!

Reb. I understand. When are we to begin?

Alv. Now—directly.

Reb. Very good. (*In a loud voice.*) This is the reward of my merits! A rascal, a pitiful scoundrel, is preferred, when a man of honor—a man who has seen service——

Chis. Hullo! Rebolledo up! All is not so well!

Reb. Who has led you to victory——

Alv. This language to me, sir?

Reb. Yes, to you, who have so grossly insulted and defrauded——

Alv. Silence! And think yourself lucky if I take no further notice of your insolence!

Reb. If I restrain myself, it is only because you are my captain, and, as such— But, 'fore God, if my cane were in my hand——

Chis. (*advancing*). Hold! Hold!

Alv. I'll show you, sir, how to talk to me in this way!

(*Draws his sword.*)

Reb. It is before your commission, not you, I retreat.

Alv. That sha'n't save you, rascal!

(*Pursues* REBOLLEDO *out.*)

Chis. Oh, I sha'n't be Madam Roulette after all! Murder! Murder! (*Exit, lamenting.*)

SCENE III. ISABEL'S *Room.*

ISABEL *and* INES.

Isab. What noise is that on the stairs?

Enter REBOLLEDO.

Reb. Sanctuary! Sanctuary!

Isab. Who are you, sir?

Enter ALVARO.

Alv. Where is the rascal?

Isab. A moment, sir! This poor man has flown to our feet for protection. I appeal to you for it; and no man, and least of all an officer, will refuse that to any woman.

Alv. I swear no other arm than that of beauty, and beauty such as yours, could have withheld me. (*To* REBOLLEDO.) You may thank the deity that has saved you, rascal!

Isab. And I thank you, sir.

Alv. And yet ungratefully slay me with your eyes in return for sparing him with my sword!

Isab. Oh, sir, do not mar the grace of a good deed by a poor compliment, and so make me less mindful of the real thanks I owe you!

Alv. Wit and modesty kiss each other, as well they may, in that lovely face. (*Kneels.*)

Isab. Heavens—my father!

Enter CRESPO *and* JUAN *with swords.*

Cres. How is this, sir? I am alarmed by cries of murder in my house—am told you have pursued a poor man up to my daughter's room; and, when I get here, expecting to find you killing a man, I find you courting a woman.

Alv. We are all born subjects to some dominion—soldiers especially to beauty. My sword, though justly raised against this man, as justly fell at this lady's bidding.

Cres. No lady, sir, if you please, but a plain peasant girl —my daughter.

Juan (*aside*). All a trick to get at her. My blood boils. (*Aloud to* ALVARO.) I think, sir, you might have seen

214

enough of my father's desire to serve you to prevent your requiting him by such an affront as this!

Cres. And, pray, who bid thee meddle, boy? Affront! What affront? The soldier affronted his captain; and if the captain has spared him for thy sister's sake, pray, what hast thou to say against it?

Alv. I think, young man, you had best consider before you impute ill intention to an officer.

Juan. I know what I know.

Cres. What! you will go on, will you?

Alv. It is out of regard for you I do not chastise him.

Cres. Wait a bit. If that were wanting, 'twould be from his father, not from you.

Juan. And, what's more, I wouldn't endure it from any one but my father.

Alv. You would not?

Juan. No! death rather than such dishonor!

Alv. What, pray, is a clodpole's idea of honor?

Juan. The same as a captain's. None in a clodpole— none in a captain.

Alv. 'Fore Heaven, I must punish this insolence!

(About to strike him.)

Cres. You must do it through me, then.

Reb. Eyes right! Don Lope!

Alv. Don Lope!

Enter Don Lope.

Lope. How now? A riot the very first thing I find on joining the regiment? What is it all about?

Alv. (*aside*). Awkward enough!

Cres. (*aside*). By the Lord, the boy would have held his own with the best of 'em!

Lope. Well! No one answers me? 'Fore God, I'll pitch the whole house, men, women, and children, out of windows, if you don't tell me at once! Here have I had to trail up your accursed stairs, and then no one will tell me what for.

Cres. Nothing, nothing at all, sir.

Lope. Nothing? That would be the worst excuse of all; but swords aren't drawn for nothing. Come, the truth!

Alv. Well, the simple fact is this, Don Lope: I am quartered upon this house, and one of my soldiers——

Lope. Well, sir, go on.

Alv. Insulted me so grossly I was obliged to draw my sword on him. He ran up here, where it seems these two girls live; and I, not knowing there was any harm, after him. At which these men, their father or brother, or some such thing, take affront. This is the whole business.

Lope. I am just come in time, then, to settle it. First, who is the soldier that began it with an act of insubordination?

Reb. What! am I to pay the piper?

Isab. (*pointing to* Rebolledo). This, sir, was the man who ran up first.

Lope. This? Handcuff him!

Reb. Me, my Lord?

Alv. (*aside to* Rebolledo). Don't blab; I'll bear you harmless.

Reb. Oh, I dare say, after being marched off with my hands behind me like a coward. Noble commander, 'twas the captain's own doing. He made me pretend a quarrel, that he might get up here to see the women.

Cres. I had some cause for quarrel, you see.

Lope. Not enough to imperil the peace of the town for, Hullo there! beat all to quarters on pain of death. And, to prevent further ill blood here, do you (*to* ALVARO) quarter yourself elsewhere till we march. I'll stop here.

Alv. I shall, of course, obey you, sir.

Cres. (*to* ISABEL). Go in. (*Exeunt* ISABEL *and* INES.) I really ought to thank you heartily for coming just as you did, sir; else I'd managed for myself.

Lope. How so?

Cres. I should have killed this popinjay.

Lope. What, sir, a captain in his Majesty's service?

Cres. Aye, a general, if he insulted me!

Lope. I tell you, whoever lays his little finger on the humblest private in the regiment, I'll hang him!

Cres. And I tell you, whoever points his little finger at my honor, I'll cut him down before hanging!

Lope. Know you not, you are bound by your allegiance to submit?

Cres. To all cost of property, yes; but of honor, no, no, no! My goods and chattels, aye, and my life, are the king's; but my honor is my own soul's, and that is—God Almighty's!

Lope. 'Fore God, there's some truth in what you say.

Cres. 'Fore God, there ought to be, for I've been some years saying it.

Lope. Well, well. I've come a long way, and this leg of mine—which I wish the devil who gave it would carry away with him!—cries for rest.

Cres. And who prevents its taking some? The same devil, I suppose, who gave you your leg, gave me a bed —which I don't want him to take away again, however— on which your leg may lie, if it like.

Lope. But did the devil, when he was about it, make your bed as well as give it?

Cres. To be sure he did.

Lope. Then I'll unmake it. Heaven knows I'm weary enough.

Cres. Heaven rest you, then.

Lope (*aside*). Devil or saint, alike he echoes me.

Cres. (*aside*). I and Don Lope never shall agree.

Tomas Yriarte

The Musical Ass

THE fable which I now present
Occurr'd to me by accident;
And whether bad or excellent,
Is merely so by accident.

A stupid ass one morning went
Into a field by accident
And cropp'd his food and was content,
Until he spied by accident
A flute, which some oblivious gent
Had left behind by accident;
When, sniffing it with eager scent,
He breathed on it by accident,
And made the hollow instrument
Emit a sound by accident.
"Hurrah! hurrah!" exclaimed the brute,
"How cleverly I play the flute!"

A fool, in spite of nature's bent,
May shine for once—by accident.

—"Fables."

The Eggs

BEYOND the sunny Philippines
An island lies, whose name I do not know;
But that's of little consequence, if so
You understand that there they had no hens,

Till, by a happy chance, a traveler,
After a while, carried some poultry there.
Fast they increased as any one could wish,
Until fresh eggs became the common dish.
But all the natives ate them boiled, they say,
Because the stranger taught no other way.
At last the experiment by one was tried—
Sagacious man!—of having his eggs fried.
And, oh, what boundless honors, for his pains,
His fruitful and inventive fancy gains!
Another, now, to have them baked devised—
Most happy thought!—and still another, spiced.
Who ever thought eggs were so delicate!
Next, some one gave his friends an omelette.
" Ah ! " all exclaimed, " what an ingenious feat ! "
But scarce a year went by, an artist shouts:
" I have it now ! Ye're all a pack of louts !
With nice tomatoes all my eggs are stewed ! "
And the whole island thought the mode so good,
That they would so have cooked them to this day,
But that a stranger, wandering out that way,
Another dish the gaping natives taught,
And showed them eggs cooked *à la Huguenot.*

Successive cooks thus proved their skill diverse,
But how shall I be able to rehearse
All of the new, delicious condiments
That luxury from time to time invents?
Soft, hard, and dropped; and now with sugar sweet,
And now boiled up with milk, the eggs they eat;
In sherbet, in preserves; at last they tickle
Their palates fanciful with eggs in pickle,

All had their day—the last was still the best.
But a grave senior thus, one day, addressed
The epicures: " Boast, ninnies, if you will,
These countless prodigies of gastric skill—
But blessings on the man who brought the hens ! "

Beyond the sunny Philippines
Our crowd of modern authors need not go
New-fangled modes of cooking eggs to show.
                                        —" *Fables.*"

The Bear, the Ape, and the Pig

A BEAR, whose dancing help'd to gain
    His own and owner's livelihood,
And whose success had made him vain
    As any dandy, stood
Upon his hinder legs to try
    The figure of a new quadrille,
When, seeing that an ape was nigh,
    He stump'd about with all his skill,
And, " Tell me how you like," he cried,
    " My dancing, for I'm always glad
To hear the truth ! " The ape replied,
    " I really think it very bad."
" 'Tis plain enough," rejoin'd the bear,
    " That envy makes you censure so;
For have I not a graceful air,
    A slender shape and limber toe ? "

Spanish Wit and Humor

But here a tasteless pig began
　To grunt applause, and said, " I vow
I've never met, in brute or man,
　With one who danced so well as thou."
The bear, on hearing this, became
　Sedate and pensive for a while;
And then, as if abash'd with shame,
　Replied, in a more humble style:
" The agile ape's rebuke might be
　Inspired by jealousy or spleen;
But, since the pig commends, I see
　How bad my dancing must have been."

Let every author think on this,
　And hold this maxim for a rule:
The worst that can befall him is
　The approbation of a fool.

　　　　　　　　　　　　—" Fables."

Manuel de los Herreros

Two Rival Lovers Gulled

Street in Front of CAMILLA'S *House.*

CAPTAIN ANDRÉS *and* LIEUTENANT MIGUEL.

Andrés. A pity the sun is not shining now! I would like to gaze upon those divine features. But on yonder corner the lamp is going out. Thither I will go. My impatience— (*He turns to the right.*)

Miguel (*turning at the same time to the left*). Her mother has certainly had a sudden attack. (*He perceives* DON ANDRÉS.) But there is somebody!

Andrés (*seeing* MIGUEL). A man!

Miguel. Who goes there?

Andrés. Make room!

Miguel. That is Andrés's voice.

Andrés. If I mistake not— Yes, it is he—Miguel.

Miguel. Captain?

Andrés. I did not expect to find you on the street at this hour. Is this your beat?

Miguel. Are you paying court to some one?

Andrés. I am, Miguel. What a girl she is! The fire of her eye, her mouth like a rose in May, and a hand——

Miguel. My beloved is without defects! So affectionate, so true! There is not another such charming girl in all Seville!

Andrés. Faithful?

Miguel. Extraordinarily so. And yours?

Andrés. A jewel! I am the happiest of lovers.

Miguel. You have no rivals?

Andrés. None. And I fear none!

Miguel. Nor do I. Do you call on her?

Andrés. No. Do you?

Miguel. I do not. Her mother is a strange person.

Andrés. The mother of my adored one is possessed of the Evil One. But what of it, if my beloved becomes mine?

Miguel. Mine gave me, this evening— Heavens—I am mad for joy—a hand!

Andrés. Mine allowed me to kiss both her hands.

Miguel. My sweetheart has retired. Her mother became ill.

Andrés. My future mother-in-law, too, was not well.

Miguel. Our conversation was interrupted, as my dear one had to sit up with the old dame.

Andrés. And meanwhile you were holding a monologue at the lattice? Strange! I have fared the same way. I fear— Tell me, your siren does not live far from here?

Miguel. No; there is her house.

Andrés (*examining the place*). Alas! My hope is gone! She has a second window opening upon another street.

Miguel. What do I hear? Infamous treason!

Andrés. A rascally intrigue! She engaged to meet us both at the same time—you at one window, me at the other.

Miguel. It is impossible! Her tenderness——

Andrés. Give me your lady's name!

Miguel. Camilla.

Andrés. Camilla. It is she! Oh, the faithless one! to play with me, to treat me thus! And yet, even if she be false, I adore her. Draw your sword and strike, or renounce her!

Manuel de los Herreros

Miguel. Do not expect me to stand back! I know that I am the favored one.

Andrés. If my constancy is thus trampled upon, I hope at least to avenge myself by killing you first, and then her.

Miguel. Let the duel start at once.

Andrés. Good fortune to the victor!

Miguel. Love will make me invincible. Now, then!

Andrés. Have a care!

(*Both fight for a few moments.* Andrés *stops.*)
Listen. Though my happiness is shaken, I do not doubt that Camilla loves me; but being, after all, an unlucky person, I might easily be pierced by a thrust of your sword. I do not for that reason shun your weapon. I am so jealous that I would fight the Cid himself. But if this duel is to be my death, the likeness of the detestable creature shall be your inheritance. Take it from my breast when I heave the last sigh, so that such a marvel may not fall into the hands of a common thief.

Miguel. If your sword despatches me, I, too, will give you— But speak: how came you by Camilla's likeness?

Andrés. She gave it to me this night, with many caresses, and I——

Miguel. Will you show it to me?

Andrés. Yes, here it is.

Miguel. What a shameful betrayal! I gave it to the false one to-night. It is my work. I painted her from memory!

Andrés. If she is not the devil's own daughter, then——

Miguel. And to me the tender, the grateful, the proud one gave this ring.

Andrés. Let me see! I tremble with rage! It is mine! It contains my hair!

225

Miguel. Your hair? And I, great heavens, have kissed it passionately!

Andrés. What has become of our love?

Miguel. A game of dice!

Andrés. Yet, even if I do feel my shame——

Miguel. Even if I do see her falsehood, I still love her!

Andrés. I still adore her!

Miguel. Thus wills my star, which I must follow!

Andrés. As great, oh, Miguel, is my infatuation!

Miguel. But does this faithless one deserve that we kill each other for her sake?

Andrés. No. Let us sheathe our swords.

Miguel. And what, I ask you, shall we do now?

Andrés. Let us settle this matter like good comrades. I do not feel the strength to abandon her to you.

Miguel. I claim her for myself.

Andrés. So do I.

Miguel. There is the difficulty.

Andrés. We will not fight for her. But I have an idea. She cannot possibly love us both with equal ardor.

Miguel. Secretly she must prefer one of us.

Andrés. Let her decide. I will abide by her decision.

Miguel. And I will renounce her if she vows to make you happy.

Andrés. So will I.

Miguel. Agreed!

Andrés. Upon honor!

Miguel. Upon honor!—" *A Female Don Juan.*"

Anonymous Author

Minguillo's Kiss

SINCE for kissing thee, Minguillo,
  Mother's ever scolding me,
Give me swiftly back, thou dear one,
  Give the kiss I gave to thee.
Give me back the kiss—that one, now;
  Let my mother scold no more;
  Let us tell her all is o'er:
What was done is all undone now.
Yes, it will be wise, Minguillo,
  My fond kiss to give to me;
Give me swiftly back, thou dear one,
  Give the kiss I gave to thee.
Give me back the kiss, for mother
  Is impatient—prithee, do!
  For that one thou shalt have two:
Give me that, and take another.
Yes, then will they be contented,
  Then can't they complain of me;
Give me swiftly back, thou dear one,
  Give the kiss I gave to thee.

José de Larra—"Figaro"

Joys of Journalism

"At last I am a journalist!" I exclaimed enthusiastically, and immediately began to conceive articles, fully determined to grind in the mortar of my criticism any writer who might be unfortunate enough to invade the territory covered by my jurisdiction. Fool that I was! I shall recount briefly my experiences, without, however, revealing the secret springs that set in motion the complicated machinery of a magazine, or lifting the veil of prestige that drapes its altars. My story is unexaggerated and impartial, and I leave the reader to judge if it be not preferable to subscribe to a periodical than to be obliged wisely and hurriedly to provide reading matter for it.

"Mr. Figaro," says the editor, "let us have an article on the stage, if you please."

Now, be it understood that I write for the public, and the public, it seems to me, deserves the truth. The comedy in question is ridiculous. The actor, A, is bad, and the actress, B, is worse. Great heavens! It never would have occurred to me to choose the stage as my subject. What is to be done when the author of a comedy pronounces it excellent and the critic acephalous? The actors will use bad language, the author's future plays will be refused, and every one will be disgusted. Who is this critic, anyhow? An incompetent, a pedant, a rascal! And all this obloquy falls on the unlucky head of the poor friend of beauty and of truth.

Oh, the joys of journalism!

José de Larra

I fly precipitately from the stage to literature. A presumptuous individual has just published a quite indigestible work. "Sir," he begins a seductive letter, "I confide in your talent and in your friendship for myself, of which I have ample proof (which unfortunately is quite true), that you will honor my work with a just and impartial criticism (by impartial he means favorable), and I hope that you will do me the honor to dine with me, in order that we may together discuss certain ideas that might be touched upon etc."

Ignore these insinuations, and you will have to choose between ingratitude and falsehood. Both vices have their stern detractors, and the wrath of at least one of them will be vented on the unlucky Figaro.

Oh, the joys of journalism!

I will translate foreign news, then. I sharpen my pen, arrange a vast pile of periodicals, and set to work. Three columns are soon written. Three columns, did I say? On the following day I look for them in the *Review,* but in vain.

"Mr. Editor, what has been done with my copy?"

"None of your business!" he replies. "Here it is. We haven't been able to use it. This piece is not suitable; that over there is out of date; the other is good, but badly translated."

"But remember that one must do this work for hours at a time, and a man gets tired!" I explain.

"If you are the sort of man who gets tired, you are no use for newspaper work."

"But my head aches already."

"The head of a good journalist never aches."

Oh, the joys of journalism!

Away with trifles, then. It seems that I am cut out for

sterner stuff. I will write a profound and instructive article
—on political economy, for instance.

"A fine article," the editor tells me, "but don't write any
more like it."

"Why not?"

"Because it will ruin my magazine. Who do you think
will read it, if it is not jocular, malicious, or superficial?
Besides, it takes up five columns—all that I have left. No,
Mr. Figaro, let us have no more scientific articles. You are
wasting your time."

Oh, the joys of journalism!

"Now, I wish you would revise these articles that have
been sent in, especially those dealing with poetical subjects."

"Yes, Mr. Editor, but I shall have to read them."

"Certainly, Mr. Figaro."

"Very good, Mr. Editor, but I would much rather recite
the whole of the Litany fifty times."

"Mr. Figaro!"

Oh, the joys of journalism!

Politics and more politics. What else is left to me? It
is true that I do not know anything about it, but what difference will that make? Shall I be the first to write igno-
rantly on politics? I set to work, then, and string together a
batch of words such as these: conferences, protocols, rights,
representation, monarchy, legality, cabinets, courts, centrali-
zation, nations, happiness, peace, illusions, treason, war, in-
expedience, belligerents, armistice, forces, unity, govern-
ments, maxims, systems, disquisitions, revolution, order,
center, left, modification, bill, reforms, etc. I write my
article, but, merciful heavens! the editor sends for me.

"Mr. Figaro, you are evidently trying to compromise me
with the ideas propounded in this article."

"I propound ideas, Mr. Editor? If so, I did not know it. What reason could I have for such a thing?"

"You had better take care."

"Pardon me, but I did not believe my political system was so—" I paused to think of an appropriate word.

"Because, if any harm should result, you will be responsible."

"I, Mr. Editor?"

Oh, the joys of journalism!

If this were only all for which poor Figaro stands responsible, it would not be so bad. Even if the author were not mediocre, nor the actor offended, nor the article displeasing, some confounded imp of a printer would be sure to make some silly mistake in spelling. And then who would be responsible? Figaro, of course! It is probable that I shall soon be obliged to print my own articles.

Oh, the joys of journalism!

And to think that I once cherished a desire to enter the journalistic field! I confess to you, dear reader, that I have a weak character, and never knew what I wanted. And this you may judge from the long list of my unfortunate writings, which, however, I shall do my best to abridge, henceforth, as much as I can.

Oh, the joys of journalism!—*The Articles.*

Don Candido Buenafe's Ambitious Son

Don Candido Buenafé is an excellent fellow, but one of those men of whom one is accustomed to speak as unlucky. He has been employed all his life in an obscure branch of the civil service, and knows just about enough to read the

Gazette, and compose, with bad syntax and worse orthography, official correspondence of a routine sort, or make extracts from legal documents. But, in spite of his lack of learning, he is ambitious that his son Tomas should grow up wiser than himself, to which end, by the way, no extraordinary efforts or sacrifices would be necessary. "I would cheerfully give," he has said many a time, newspaper in hand, "half of my salary to be able to write a political article as good as this. What a clever man the author of this must be, and how he convinces one with his arguments! Yes, I would give half of my life, and the other half, too, if my son Tomas might some day do as well."

Imbued with this idea, he had the boy taught Latin, and later sent him to a French master, "because," as he said, "if you know French you know all that need be known"; and he would add, "There are plenty of learned pundits in the country who know nothing else." In two months the little angel, who was fourteen years old at the time, learned to translate badly and read defectively, "Calypso se trouvait inconsolable du départ d'Ulysse," and then it was that he and his papa made me a visit, the interesting details of which I here set forth for the entertainment of my readers.

"Mr. Figaro," said Don Candido, greeting me cordially, "let me present to you my son Tomas, who knows Latin. You may not be ignorant of the fact that I am training him for a literary career, in order that he may rescue the family name from obscurity. Ah, Mr. Figaro, when I see him famous, I shall die happy."

Tomas then made so awkward a bow that I could do no less than found great hopes on his literary prowess. But his appearance and speech differed not at all from those of other young men of the day. He told me that it was true that he

was only fourteen years old, but that he knew the world and
the human heart *comme ma poche,* that all women were alike,
that he was very *blasé,* and that he was deceived by none;
that Voltaire was a great man, and that no one had laughed
more than he at *Compère Mathieu,* since his papa, desirous
of his attaining knowledge, had allowed him to read any
book that might fall into his hands. Touching politics, he
added, "I and Chateaubriand agree"; and, in conclusion,
he chattered about nations and revolutions as he might have
recounted the doings of his school friends.

"The boys of the nineteenth century," said I to myself,
"seem to reach old age before they have been young."

My two friends, the ancient youth and the youthful old
man, then seated themselves, and Don Candido took from
his pocket a thick package.

"My visit has two objects," he said. "As for the first,
Tomas having made great strides in French, I have told
him to translate a comedy. He has done so, and here it is."

"What!"

"Yes, sir. Certain passages have been left in blank, since
he had no other dictionary than Sobrino's, and——"

"Yes?"

"You will undoubtedly be kind enough to alter anything
that seems to you incorrect; and as you are familiar with
the steps necessary to take in order to put it on the stage,
and the——"

"Ah! you wish to have it produced?"

"Most certainly. You see, the royalties will be for him."

"Yes, sir," interrupted the boy, "and papa has promised
me a dress suit as soon as the tragedy on which I am now
working is finished."

"Tragedy?"

"Yes, sir, in eleven scenes. You know, in Paris they no longer construct these works in acts, but in scenes. It is a romantic tragedy. Classicism is the death of genius, as of course you know. Do you think there is any chance of its being given?"

"Well, why not?"

"Let me tell you," put in Don Candido, "he has already written a descriptive comedy."

"I beg your pardon," added Tomas, "when I wrote it, I had not read Victor Hugo, nor had I the experience that I now possess."

"Indeed!"

"Yes, my son wrote the comedy, and we sent it to a man who makes a specialty of reading plays. He said that it was all right, and that he would send it to the censor. So I suppose he sent it."

"Excuse me, papa, but it was lost, you remember."

"Oh, yes, certainly, it was lost; and as we could not find it anywhere, we had to make another copy, and sent it to the censor."

"Papa, you are mistaken; first we sent it to the civil bureau."

"So we did, and from there it went to the ecclesiastical censor, was then returned to the civil bureau, and finally got to the political censor. In a word, in six months it came back to us prohibited."

"Prohibited!"

"Yes, sir; and why, I don't know, because my comedy——"

"It may be that they did well, Mr. Figaro. My son always writes with a purpose! But is it not enough to say that his mother nearly died of laughing when she read it, and that I wept with joy?"

"The second object that brings us here," Don Candido presently resumed, "is that you may give my Tomas some good advice, for I have already told him that he should not restrict himself to plays; that the field of literature is very vast, and that the temple of fame has many doors."

"You are right, friend Candido. But allow me to tell your son the best way to become famous. Do not write anything for a long time. Silence is literary aristocracy, and I say to you that if you follow my advice there will come a day when the words will be on everybody's lips, 'Don Tomas, yes, Don Tomas is a wise man.' After that you will be able with perfect confidence to deluge the public with comedies, essays, and commentaries. Everything will then be read with avidity, if only it be from the hand of Don Tomas. If you have no desire for fame, and wish to take the short road to publicity, you must act quite otherwise. Steep yourself in comic writers; have a correspondent in Paris, and send for a new comedy of Scribe every week; worm yourself into the columns of the newspapers, and write that everything is as it should be, and that we are all saints. Make arrangements with some publisher, who will give you four or five pesos a volume for translations of Walter Scott, which you can do at odd moments. That they may be badly translated matters not at all, for neither the publisher nor any other Christian will understand them. That's the way to become famous, Don Tomas."

At this point Don Candido fell into my arms, and, taking Tomas by the hand, said:

"See, my son, how wisely the gentleman speaks. Now give thanks to your protector. I suspected it all: you need know no more than you know already. How fortunate, Mr. Figaro! My son's career is made. Essays, comedies, novels, translations! And all through knowing French! Oh, French! French! Ah! and magazines? Did you not also mention magazines, Mr. Figaro?"

"Yes, my friend, and magazines too," I concluded, conducting the pair to the door, and bidding them farewell. "Only I warn you not to put too much faith in them, as they may not always be in existence. But remember the rest of my advice, for that is the road to fame."

—The Essays.

Antonio Ribot y Fontseré

Maximum and Minimum

ABOUT the middle of the last century there flourished in Canterbury two physicians, by name of Thompson and Kinster. The former was a man of more, the latter a man of less; the one knew no arithmetical rules save those of addition and multiplication, the other only acknowledged those of subtraction and division. Thompson ignored existence and being; everything seemed to him trifling, small, insignificant, and in this point of view he was the antithesis of Kinster, who, seeking everywhere simplicity, and believing that existence is the greatest of evils, tried to reduce everything to its lowest possible point of restriction, to the indispensable and the absolutely necessary, and his life was a long series of labors consecrated to the quest of the irreducible minimum. The systems of Thompson and Kinster were as far asunder as heaven and the bottomless pit, as infinity and zero.

Each applied the spirit of his system to the smallest details of his daily life. Thompson spoke always in periphrase, expressed all his ideas by means of circumlocution and redundance, and, not content to employ the largest number of words possible, he even chose the longest syllables, and in his habitual conversation gave the preference to the most intricate constructions. His professional visits partook more of the nature of the lover than of the physician. He hardly ever made use of heroic remedies, for the reason that they could not be prescribed in huge quantities; and if, perchance, he put some patient on diet, it nearly always had the effect of hastening his victim to the hands of the undertaker. The good doctor reasoned thus: Where is the invalid whose state could be prejudiced by eating a grain of rice or an infinitesimal fiber of chicken? And where is the invalid who, after having consumed one grain of rice or one fiber of chicken, could not with impunity partake of another grain or another fiber? If he can take one, then why not two, three, or four? And thus, from grain to grain and from fiber to fiber, he finally consented to his patient satisfying his hunger with a pound of rice or a whole chicken. He employed the same basis of calculation when computing the number of persons that a given space would hold. The application of this theory to practise was often followed by serious consequences. . . .

One day he invited seventeen of his friends to accompany him on an excursion into the country. He insisted that they all enter one coach, which would hold six with difficulty, and to certain suggestions which were made to him on the impenetrability of matter, he replied, with his customary optimism, that if six could enter, why not seven, and if seven, why not eight? And so, one after the other, he forced in the whole seventeen. The inert mass of crushed, smothered, bruised humanity, unable to speak or even breathe, would certainly have succumbed to the doctor's obstinacy if the coach, shortly after leaving Canterbury, had not burst like a bombshell.

The explosion was accompanied by loud screams of agony from its occupants. Those who were nearest the windows were shot out with the impetus of water squirted from a syringe. The state of those who had first entered the vehicle was pitiful. The squeezing process had so increased their longitude at the expense of their latitude that their mothers would hardly have known them.

Notwithstanding this catastrophe, the doctor would not hear of giving up his pastoral excursion, but the horse, a mere skeleton of a beast, evidently thought otherwise. The driver, following the doctor's orders, did his best, but the horse rebelled at Thompson's theories, and would rather have been killed a thousand times than budge a single inch. When he saw that he could not overcome such obstinate resistance, the doctor made his guests get out and follow the coach on foot. This meant a walk of several miles, and few of them felt sufficient confidence in their legs for such a task; but no one dared to place himself in open objection to Thompson's caprices, for all knew that he was capable of shooting his best friend with as much indifference as he would have prescribed half an ounce of cream of tartar for a patient. The party covered a mile of the distance without mishap, and then the strength of many of them began to fail. Thompson, noticing this, encouraged the most laggard with his habitual cure-all. "Just a step more is nothing, two steps are nothing, and a man who can take two steps can take three; and, as we know that a few steps are nothing at all, we can walk any distance." As a matter of fact, he felt very tired himself, but his faith in his doctrines would have enabled him to walk round the world.

But there finally arrived a time when the whole company had reached the end of their strength. They stopped, and determined to go no farther. "Damn!" said the doctor, enraged by their decision, and put a hand into each of his side-pockets. All trembled, and breathed a prayer, for they believed their last hour had come. There was a moment of anguish, of mortal terror; but soon their faces cleared, for Thompson withdrew his hands from his pockets as empty as they had been before. "Damnation!" he muttered, "I have left my pistols at home. Nevertheless, my rage will take the place of powder, and my fists will do the duty of bullets."

But this bravado frightened nobody, for what is one against seventeen? The doctor soon saw himself attacked on all sides by his infuriated guests, who pommeled him until they were tired. When they left him he was spouting curses like some blasphemous geyser. It took him two days to return to Canterbury, where we shall leave him for the present.

Kinster, with his theory of the minimum, was no less extravagant than Thompson with his theory of the maximum. He had devoted himself to the dictionary with much assiduity in order to memorize the shortest words, and had converted his brain into a monosyllabic magazine. He talked in monosyllables, he wrote in monosyllables, and in his letters he abbreviated even these. His visits were as short as those of a postman or a newsboy; he was hardly inside a house before he was out again and into another; he entered and left almost at the same time. He prescribed the most harmless remedies in fractional doses, so that he might have been called the founder of homeopathy, if his point of view had not been entirely distinct from that of the homeopathists. Kinster believed that a grain of anything was quite as efficacious as a pound, on which basis he calculated that if a grain was as good as a pound, why was not the infinitesimal part of a grain as good as a grain? And so on. By this process of reasoning, he ended by leaving his patient without any medicine; in which habits, by the way, he might be emulated to advantage by a number of physicians of my acquaintance.

Antonio Ribot y Fontseré

With respect to surgery, Kinster was a terrible operator. Convinced that existence is the worst of evils, and desiring to reduce it among men to the lowest possible point, on the appearance of an ordinary pimple or an insignificant scratch he at once proceeded to amputate the offending member. His system lasted for some time, and the tourist who in those days visited Canterbury was horrorstruck by the sight of universal mutilation, men everywhere without eyes, without ears, without arms, all dismal witnesses of the devastating system of Dr. Kinster. More than one traveler was moved to ask if in Canterbury there existed a peculiar race of men who came into the world less richly endowed with members than the rest of mankind. Fortunately, Kinster's system fell into utter disrepute, and the good doctor, finding no more patients to visit, devoted his time to the chase. But in this he was even more unlucky than he had been in the exercise of his profession. In pursuance of his theory, he loaded his gun with an almost invisible pinch of powder and a single shot of the smallest size. He would take a handful of shot, and say, "Will not the bird fall as readily if there be one shot less? And if one less doesn't matter, what difference will it make if two are missing?" In this way he gradually discarded the shot until the charge was reduced to a single pellet, and frequently none at all. This did not prevent him, however, from firing at royal eagles, nor did it lessen his disappointment at having to return invariably with empty hands. . . .

The time came when Thompson and Kinster married. But do not think, gentle reader, that they married each other. Thompson married one woman and Kinster a second, and neither physician allowed matrimony to interfere with his extravagant theory. Thus it was that Thompson, in his love of magnitude, wedded the largest woman in England; and Kinster, the champion of the minimum, took for his wife the smallest. Thompson's wife was known throughout the United Kingdom as the Elephant, while Kinster's spouse rejoiced in the sobriquet of the Thumb. But it was hardly to be expected that any woman, large or small, could suffer for long the whims of our medical friends, who practised their exaggerated theories down to the most insignificant domestic details, and even to those intimacies which are essentially matrimonial. The Elephant and the Thumb died, but not without each leaving to her husband a living testimonial to her fecundity. They died within a year of their marriage, and, by one of those singular freaks of Nature which cannot be explained, the Elephant presented Thompson with a daughter who, at fifteen years of age, was so small that she might have been the offspring of the Thumb; while on the same day a daughter was born to Kinster, who, when she had reached her fifteenth year, was so large that she resembled no one so much as the Elephant.

See, therefore, by what methods much wiser than the dispositions of mankind does Providence unite like with unlike, even when as diametrically opposed as Thompson and Kinster. When Thompson lost his Elephant he gave up hope of ever finding another woman of such impressive stature, and resolved to remain a widower all his days; and for the same reason Kinster also despaired of ever again meeting another Thumb. But when Thompson saw the corpulent daughter of Kinster, and Kinster the diminutive daughter of Thompson, their fine resolutions suddenly changed, and reciprocal matrimony was agreed upon. Their respective daughters fell into the arrangement with an enthusiasm not difficult to explain. For to the naturally abstemious daughter of Thompson, who was obliged by the rigorous system of her father to fill her stomach with far more food than her capacity permitted, every meal was a torture from which she would have done anything to free herself, and this was undoubtedly the motive that caused her to give her hand to Kinster. The daughter of the last named, on the other hand, naturally robust and voracious, and forced to subject herself to a rigid adherence to the starvation theories of her father, saw in Thompson her liberating angel, little dreaming that in escaping starvation she was courting a worse fate.

The double wedding having been celebrated, Thompson and Kinster, in order to be near their respective daughters, decided that all should live together as a single family. It did not take many days for the house to become a bedlam. The two physicians struck each other as even more extravagant than they would have appeared to a rational being, and from morning until night they argued over their ridiculous theories of the maximum and the minimum. Thompson's daughter began to feel the gnawing pangs of hunger, and to regret her past gorgings, and Kinster's daughter implored Heaven to relieve her fulness, and would have sacrificed anything in the world to be placed again on the old ascetic diet. Sometimes, fortunately, the systems of Kinster and Thompson neutralized each other, but this only happened as a sequel to horrid struggles and mutual recriminations, which nearly always ended tragically.

The scene generally took place when they were dining in the open air. If, for instance, it was rice that they were eating, Dr. Thompson would ply his wife with grain after grain and spoonful after spoonful, until she could hardly sit up, and sometimes the food would be seen coming out of her eyes and ears; and this would so enrage Dr. Kinster that he could not refrain from calling his brother-in-law barbarous and brutal, although he well knew Thompson's irascible and overbearing disposition. Then the two physicians would stigmatize each other as visionaries and fools, and after a sputter of epithets that sounded like a volley of musketry, they would supplement their words with blows. At this point the women, instead of trying to separate their husbands and fathers, even when almost exhausted, would take advantage of the scuffle to improve by the situation. While Kinster's wife would ravenously devour everything on the table, Thompson's better half would hurry away, and escape from the odious stuffing. . . .

I cannot now record the multitude of curious and strange stories born of the eccentricities of Thompson and Kinster. I present only one incident, which I think will sufficiently illustrate the character of the two physicians. One day, after a more serious affray than usual, from which both parties emerged with bloody noses and faces covered with scars and bruises, the two combatants fell to the ground, crestfallen and taciturn, and gave themselves up to profound meditation. After an hour of silence, Thompson absent-mindedly asked Kinster a question, which started the following dialogue:

" What are you thinking about, Kinster? "

" And you, Thompson, what are your thoughts? "

" I," said Thompson, " was seeking for something more immense than immensity, more infinite than infinity, more eternal than eternity."

" You're a fool! " said Kinster, between his teeth.

" And what were you seeking? " asked Thompson.

" I was trying to find nothing, absolute nothing, something which is less than nothing."

Antonio Ribot y Fontseré

" How absurd! " exclaimed Thompson. " Nothing! As if
we did not see it everywhere, more's the pity! Do you think
that you are something, that I am something, that what you
hear, what you see, what you touch is something; that the
world we live in, the generations that are gone, are something? The world was made from nothing, and from
nothing can be made only nothing. My search for something nearly drives me mad, yet I never find anything.
Nothing is followed by an imperceptible point which is
also nothing, and to this point is added another point, and
so on, and many of these points united form that which
you call something, but this something that you see is always
nothing. Everything is nothing. Generations pass and fall
into dust, and in the end even the dust disappears. Oh, that
it were possible to make of all mankind that has gone a
single generation, and of that generation a single man, one
single individual! And even then, that collective and syn-
thetic individual would seem insignificant and also nothing,
and he would in fact be nothing."

" He is quite unnecessary, Thompson, this individual whom
you wish to see realized, because everything in the world is
superfluous, even to the world itself. God formed the world
from nothing, because nothing was before anything. You
see the generations die, and I see them renewed. Everything is regenerated and is never extinguished; what you
think is disappearance is only change of form. Man repro-
duces himself, and even when he remains no more than a
corpse, he is still converting himself into an infinity of
generations. There are some who embalm the dead to preserve them. Actually they destroy them; by embalming,
they take life from matter, kill the dead. They desire that
the corpse shall not decay, and yet decay is the only life

that remains to it. From every fiber, from every atom, rise infinite generations, who die in their turn, but are not extinguished; take another form, but are not destroyed. Oh, if I only knew that death and annihilation were synonymous terms, I would have committed suicide years ago! But I can at least exist as little as possible. I will not shorten the time that Providence has apportioned to me to live in this world in body and soul, but I can diminish myself, restrict my actions, reduce myself, it may be, to an indivisible point."

There was a moment of silence, broken only by a burst of laughter from Thompson. Then Kinster rose from his chair, took Thompson by the hand, and said to him:

" Follow me."

Thompson followed him.

The two physicians entered the study, from which they first expelled their respective wives, one of whom was voraciously devouring food, and the other vomiting violently. As the women went out they noticed that Kinster gave signs of a strange agitation. The force of an overpowering curiosity glued them to the threshold. From within they heard groans and cries that would have melted the heart of a tiger, accompanied by the metallic rasping of a saw. This went on for three hours, at the end of which time Thompson came out, covered with sweat and blood, carrying a pile of severed legs, arms, and other mutilated members. In order to reduce himself to the lowest possible minimum, Dr. Kinster had made him amputate everything that he did not believe absolutely necessary to his existence. He had caused to be removed both arms and legs, the nose, one eye and both ears, and half of both the upper and lower sets of teeth. These terrible operations were consummated without disrobing the patient, for the members which Thompson carried still wore the usual garments of their owner. When the two women realized the awful significance of the sight they swooned away.

It might seem impossible that Kinster could survive the atrocious pain of the surgeon's knife, but Kinster, as well as Thompson, succumbed to a cold, or rather to the method of its treatment under his ridiculous system. Kinster, in the act of bleeding himself, lost, drop by drop, all the blood in his body, and died like a butchered ox. Thompson, on the other hand, desired that a pound of blood be taken from him, but, as in his eyes a drop was nothing, and if one drop was nothing, two drops were also nothing, and nothing was the same as a pound, he ended by not bleeding himself at all, and shortly afterward gave up the ghost. Their wives survived them, and, although neither of them ever alluded to their wedded existence, it is fairly safe to assert that they did not much regret the death of their husbands.

—*The Periodical " La Risa."*

Eccentric Britons

I ONCE knew an Englishman who was poorer than a retired Spanish sublieutenant, and more parsimonious than an old-clothes man. If, perchance, he managed to lay hold of a couple of pennies, he would put aside three halfpence for possible contingencies, and satisfy his wants with the remaining halfpenny. It happened, one day, that he was fortunate enough, with the assistance of an intelligent Newfoundland dog, which, by the way, he loved like a brother, to save from drowning a nobleman's daughter who had fallen into the Thames. Ten years afterward he unexpectedly received from the girl's father a gift of two hundred thousand pounds sterling. If this joyful announcement produced any change in the mind of the beneficiary, it certainly could not be read in his countenance. On the following day his creditors called on him in a body to offer their congratulations; but what was their astonishment to see him lying on the floor of his room bathed in his own blood, dead! Near the body they found a letter containing these words:

" No one is responsible for my death, nor yet for my misfortune. In the act of self-destruction I was happy. I possessed health and riches. Nevertheless, I wanted to kill myself, in the first place, because it was my pleasure so to do, and, in the second place, because since infancy it has been my dearest wish to have a capital of one hundred thousand pounds sterling, and I now find myself in possession of double that sum. I leave half of my wealth to my Newfoundland dog, in order that he may gratify to the top of his bent his taste for tunny-fish, of which he is passionately fond; and the other half I leave to him who shall take upon himself the responsibility of purchasing tunny-fish for my dog. (Signed) GREY."

It is hardly necessary to state that all those who found the last will and testament of the defunct expressed themselves as delighted to fulfil its conditions. It was noteworthy, however, that the dog, which was present during the reading of his master's letter, that affected him so directly, did not give vent to the least manifestation of joy. This indifference of the dog attracted a great deal of attention in London, and even caused excitement, especially on the Stock Exchange. The will of the defunct was declared invalid, and, in order to avoid complications, the two hundred thousand pounds sterling were returned to the coffers of their original owner.

The noble lord, who thus found himself in possession of a sum he had considered gone forever, thought of no better way of using it than to satisfy a caprice, the result of which was to make him famous throughout the United Kingdom as an eccentric. He proposed a wager to a wealthy merchant that he could not sell two hundred sovereigns, offering them for sale one at a time during a period of six hours on one of the most busy thoroughfares of the capital. This proposition caught the merchant, as it would have caught any one, and he accepted the wager, which was for nothing less than two hundred thousand pounds sterling, perfectly convinced that it was impossible for him to lose.

They chose a court holiday, on which immense crowds passed over Westminster Bridge on their way to St. James'. The merchant and the nobleman placed themselves at one end of the bridge, holding between them a large coffer filled with sovereigns. "Pounds sterling for sale!" cried the merchant in a loud voice; and the lord for his part did nothing else but laugh; for such were the stipulated conditions. The people passed on with such words as, "Great heavens! what an absurdly simple trick! Sovereigns for sale! What sort of coins do you think they are?"

The merchant was in despair. A casual stroller took up one of the sovereigns and looked at it closely, but at last, noticing the laughter that the lord pretended he could not repress, threw back the coin, saying, "They are a very good imitation, but they don't deceive me."

"Pounds sterling for sale!" shouted the merchant unceasingly, but the more he repeated the phrase, the more the public cried out upon what they considered an outrageous fraud directed against their pockets. The performance lasted from nine in the morning until three in the afternoon, the merchant shouting and the lord laughing.

The end of it was that the former lost his bet.

Only two sovereigns were sold, and even those were believed bad by the student who bought them, his object being to get them exchanged in some of his low haunts. When he found that they were taken without question, he hurried back to Westminster at the top of his speed to purchase more, but he arrived too late; the lord and the merchant had disappeared. This did not surprise the student, because he knew that such good and cheap wares could be disposed of in a moment; but he bitterly regretted having neglected to profit by a chance that would have enriched him at small cost.—*The Periodical " La Risa."*

Juan M. Villergas

The Friend that Sticketh Closer than a Brother

For two months I had been unable to pay my landlady her rent, and I now found myself penniless and without prospects of getting money from any source. The poor woman was kind-hearted and discreet, and, knowing my position, she respected it as long as she could; but there came a day when she could hold out no longer, and she begged me at least to pay her something on account, even if I could not liquidate the whole of the debt. I put on my hat, and went out to see if I could find something. There was not much use trying to borrow, for I knew that all my friends were about as bare of pocket as I was. I turned down toward the Buena-dicha quarter, little caring where I went, and was just beginning to ponder over ways and means, when I saw a man coming toward me with open arms. "Thank God!" I burst out, "I have stumbled on good fortune unawares." But what was my disappointment to find that I was shaking hands with a well-remembered friend of my childhood!

"You cannot imagine how delighted I am to meet you!" he said. "I have just arrived, know no one in the city, and by an unfortunate oversight have left my purse at home."

I did not know how to extricate myself from my embarrassing position. I could hardly allow the man to sleep on the streets; that would be an atrocity; and if my invitation bore the appearance of coolness, he would not accept it. So I showed him the usual cordialities.

"My dear friend," said I, "there is little that I can do for you, but I trust you will make my house your own," mentioning the street and number.

"I shall take great pleasure in accepting your courteous invitation for the time I may be staying in Madrid," he replied. "I have friends who would receive me very gladly, but I would rather go with you than with any of them."

"I shall be delighted to have you, but I cannot offer you very much."

"No matter at all; even if there is nothing but soup, we shall enjoy the soup."

Cold perspiration broke out on my forehead. But he left me no time for reflection. He took my hand in a grip that bade fair to crunch the bones, and hardly was this agony over before he clasped me in his arms in such a manner as to utterly deprive me of breath for the space of five minutes.

"What number did you say? I shall see you later, then."

When I returned to the house I found my landlady in a pleasanter mood, for she had succeeded in borrowing two hundred reals. I could not at once bring myself to enlighten her as to the result of my expedition and the unfortunate meeting in the Buena-dicha, but my friend saved me the trouble by ringing the door-bell loudly, and taking possession of the house, with the words:

"Pardon me for being a little late; I fear that I have kept you waiting."

I had to conceal my shame and tell the landlady the circumstances, but she, poor woman, was made of such good stuff that she said at once:

"Never mind! We will eat what there is. I will sleep in the attic, and your friend may have my room."

But my good friend was so dainty that nothing suited him. The next day he complained that the bed was hard. I took counsel with the landlady, which resulted in a decision to offer the dear fellow an additional mattress—namely, mine, the only remaining one in the establishment. He accepted like a lord, as though he were conferring a great favor on me. Thereafter, with nothing but a doubled-up old shawl between the wire and my body, my nights were miserable.

The dinners were especially obnoxious to the gentleman's delicate taste. Everything was either insipid or too salty.

"I really don't understand how you endure this," he said. "These women are such fools that they don't know their right hand from the left."

I was on pins and needles. More than once I was tempted to tell him to go to the devil; but I reflected that he was, after all, my guest, and that he would soon conclude his affairs and leave me in peace.

One morning, after having read the newspaper in bed (the subscription for the said periodical having been paid by the landlady), he got up in a good humor.

"I have good news for you," he said. "To-morrow you will entertain my wife, her little girl, and baby, and two of my brothers. I hasten to inform you because I know how much you will enjoy their visit."

And he went on describing his family.

My emotions would furnish material for many volumes. Imagine the frantic efforts of myself and my landlady to find beds and sustenance for all that brood; imagine that it stayed with me for six months, and then tell me if my life will be long enough to liquidate the debts incurred in that period, and if I deserve to be damned even though I should die in mortal sin.

As I was leaving the house one morning I almost ran into a man who was inquiring for my friend. Hoping to learn something that might liberate me from the pest that had invaded my home, I waited at the door and heard the following dialogue:

"Are you going to pay what you owe me?"

"But, my good man, I have not a farthing."

"That may or may not be, but I shall send a sheriff to seize anything he can find."

"Now, what is the use of that, when I offer to pay as soon as I can? It is not necessary to deprive me of my tables and my chairs and everything in the house which belongs to me and for which I owe nobody."

"Then, sir, I will go at once to the judge."

"Only wait a few days. In the meantime my servant, whom you met as you entered, will return. I will write to my steward, and——"

I did not allow him to finish the sentence. My fury knew no bounds. "I am your servant, am I!" I broke in. "Just take yourselves out of that door, or I will throw you out the window."

And they actually evacuated the house, asking a thousand pardons. As my friend was walking away he turned, and said:

"I trust that this little misunderstanding will not affect our friendship."

And he shook my hand so warmly that I can hardly hold the pen to write this story.

Pedro de Alarcon

Courting by Invective

WHILE the peasants who had saluted the magistrate were continuing their talk, Frasquita carefully sprinkled and swept the paved place which served as a courtyard to the mill, and placed half a dozen chairs where the vine-leaves of the arbor were still thickest. Tio Lucas had climbed upon the arbor for the purpose of cutting the finest bunches of grapes, and arranged them artistically in a basket.

"You know, Frasquita," said Tio Lucas from the top of the arbor, "the magistrate has fallen in love with you, and his motives are bad."

"I told you so a long time ago," answered the woman from the north. "But let him sigh. Take care you don't fall, Lucas!"

"Don't be afraid. I am holding on. He evidently likes your looks."

"You had better stop your gossiping," she interrupted him. "I know only too well who likes me and who does not. If I only knew as well why you do not like me."

"Well, that is too much! Because you are so ugly!" answered Tio Lucas.

"Listen! Ugly and the rest of it, I have a mind to climb the arbor and throw you down head first!"

"It is much more probable that I would not let you go down again without first swallowing you alive."

"There we are now! And if by chance my admirers came and saw us, they might very likely say we were a couple of apes."

"And in saying so they would hit the nail on the head, for you are a real ape, and so handsome; and I look like an ape with my hump."

"Which I like very much indeed."

"Then the magistrate's ought to please you´ better yet, because it is still larger than mine."

"Well, well! Look here, Master Lucas, don't be so jealous!"

"I jealous of the old fop? On the contrary, I am glad he is in love with you."

"Why?"

"Because sin brings its own punishment. You will never love him, and meanwhile I am the real magistrate of the city."

"Look at the vain fellow! But just suppose that I learn to love him. Stranger things have happened in this world."

"That would be a matter of little concern to me."

"Why?"

"Because in that case you would not be yourself any more, and not being what you are, or at least what I took you to be, I would not care a rap if you went wrong."

"But what would you do in such a case?"

"I? Well, I must confess I don't know, because I should then be a different person from what I am now, and cannot imagine what I might think then."

"And why would you be a different person?"

"Because I am now a man who believes in you as he believes in himself, and whose whole life centers in this belief. Consequently, when I cease to believe in you I should either die or be transformed into another being, and live in a different manner from what I do now. It would seem to me as if I had just been born, and my sentiments

would undergo a change. I do not know what I should do
with you then. Perhaps I should laugh, and turn my back
upon you; perhaps I should not know you; perhaps— But
look! what satisfaction are we likely to find in getting out
of temper for nothing? What does it matter to us if all
the magistrates in the world make love to you? Are you
not my Frasquita?"

"Yes, you old barbarian," answered Frasquita, laughing
heartily. "I am your Frasquita, and you are the Lucas of
my heart, uglier than a baboon, with more talent than any
other man, better than bread, and whom I love more than—
Well, you just come down from the arbor, and you will find
out what that 'I love' means. Come prepared to have your
ears boxed, and to be pinched as often as you have hairs on
your head!"—"*The Three-Cornered Hat.*"

Captain Veneno's Proposal of Marriage

"GREAT heavens! What a woman!" cried the captain,
and stamped with fury. "Not without reason have I been
trembling and in fear of her from the first time I saw her!
It must have been a warning of fate that I stopped playing
Ecarté with her. It was also a bad omen that I passed so
many sleepless nights. Was there ever mortal in a worse
perplexity than I am? How can I leave her alone without
a protector, loving her, as I do, more than my own life?
And, on the other hand, how can I marry her, after all my
declaimings against marriage?" Then, turning to Augustias—"What would they say of me in the club? What
would people say of me, if they met me in the street with

a woman on my arm, or if they found me at home, just about to feed a child in swaddling-clothes? I—to have children? To worry about them? To live in eternal fear that they might fall sick or die? Augustias, believe me, as true as there is a God above us, I am absolutely unfit for it! I should behave in such a way that after a short while you would call upon Heaven either to be divorced or to become a widow. Listen to my advice: do not marry me, even if I ask you."

" What a strange creature you are," said the young woman, without allowing herself to be at all discomposed, and sitting very erect in her chair. " All that you are only telling to yourself! From what do you conclude that I wish to be married to you; that I would accept your offer, and that I should not prefer living by myself, even if I had to work day and night, as so many girls do who are orphans?"

" How do I come to that conclusion?" answered the captain with the greatest candor. " Because it cannot be otherwise. Because we love each other. Because we are drawn to each other. Because a man such as I, and a woman such as you, cannot live in any other way! Do you suppose I do not understand that? Don't you suppose I have reflected on it before now? Do you think I am indifferent to your good name and reputation? I have spoken plainly in order to speak, in order to fly from my own conviction, in order to examine whether I can escape from this terrible dilemma which is robbing me of my sleep, and whether I can possibly find an expedient so that I need not marry you —to do which I shall finally be compelled, if you stand by your resolve to make your way alone!"

" Alone! Alone!" repeated Augustias roguishly. " And why not with a worthier companion? Who tells you that

I shall not some day meet a man whom I like, and who is not afraid to marry me?"

"Augustias! let us skip that!" growled the captain, his face turning scarlet.

"And why should we not talk about it?"

"Let us pass over that, and let me say, at the same time, that I will murder the man who dares to ask for your hand. But it is madness on my part to be angry without any reason. I am not so dull as not to see how we two stand. Shall I tell you? We love each other. Do not tell me I am mistaken! That would be lying. And here is the proof: if you did not love me, I, too, should not love you! Let us try to meet one another half-way. I ask for a delay of ten years. When I shall have completed my half century, and when, a feeble old man, I shall have become familiar with the idea of slavery, then we will marry without any one knowing about it. We will leave Madrid, and go to the country, where we shall have no spectators, where there will be nobody to make fun of me. But until this happens, please take half of my income secretly, and without any human soul ever knowing anything about it. You continue to live here, and I remain in my house. We will see each other, but only in the presence of witnesses—for instance, in society. We will write to each other every day. So as not to endanger your good name, I will never pass through this street, and on Memorial Day only we will go to the cemetery together with Rosa."

Augustias could not but smile at the last proposal of the good captain, and her smile was not mocking, but contented and happy, as if some cherished hope had dawned in her heart, as if it were the first ray of the sun of happiness which was about to rise in her heaven! But being a woman—

though as brave and free from artifices as few of them—
she yet managed to subdue the signs of joy rising within
her. She acted as if she cherished not the slightest hope,
and said with a distant coolness which is usually the special
and genuine sign of chaste reserve:

"You make yourself ridiculous with your peculiar conditions. You stipulate for the gift of an engagement-ring,
for which nobody has yet asked you."

"I know still another way out—for a compromise, but
that is really the last one. Do you fully understand, my
young lady from Aragon? It is the last way out, which a
man, also from Aragon, begs leave to explain to you."

She turned her head and looked straight into his eyes,
with an expression indescribably earnest, captivating, quiet,
and full of expectation.

The captain had never seen her features so beautiful and
expressive; at that moment she looked to him like a queen.

"Augustias," said, or rather stammered, this brave soldier, who had been under fire a hundred times, and who had
made such a deep impression on the young girl through
his charging under a rain of bullets like a lion, "I have
the honor to ask for your hand on one certain, essential,
unchangeable condition. To-morrow morning—to-day—as
soon as the papers are in order—as quickly as possible. I
can live without you no longer!"

The glances of the young girl became milder, and she
rewarded him for his decided heroism with a tender and
bewitching smile.

"But I repeat that it is on one condition," the bold war-
rior hastened to repeat, feeling that Augustias's glances
made him confused and weak.

"On what condition?" asked the young girl, turning fully

round, and now holding him under the witchery of her sparkling black eyes.

"On the condition," he stammered, "that, in case we have children, we send them to the orphanage. I mean—on this point I will never yield. Well, do you consent? For Heaven's sake, say yes!"

"Why should I not consent to it, Captain Veneno?" answered Augustias, with a peal of laughter. "You shall take them there yourself, or, better still, we both of us will take them there. And we will give them up without kissing them, or anything else! Don't you think we shall take them there?" Thus spoke Augustias, and looked at the captain with exquisite joy in her eyes.

The good captain thought he would die of happiness; a flood of tears burst from his eyes; he folded the blushing girl in his arms, and said, "So I am lost?"

"Irretrievably lost, Captain Veneno," answered Augustias. . . .

One morning in May, 1852—that is, four years after the scene just described—a friend of mine, who told me this story, stopped his horse in front of a mansion on San Francisco Avenue, in Madrid; he threw the reins to his groom, and asked the long-coated footman who met him at the door, "Is your master at home?"

"If your Honor will be good enough to walk up-stairs, he will find him in the library. His Excellency does not like to have visitors announced. Everybody can go up to him directly."

"Fortunately I know the house thoroughly," said the stranger to himself, while he mounted the stairs. "In the library! Well, well, who would have thought of Captain Veneno ever taking to the sciences?"

Wandering through the rooms, the visitor met another servant, who repeated, " The master is in the library." And at last he came to the door of the room in question, opened it quickly, and stood, almost turned to stone for astonishment, before the remarkable group which offered to his view.

In the middle of the room, on the carpet which covered the floor, a man was crawling on all-fours. On his back rode a little fellow about three years old, who was kicking the man's sides with his heels. Another small boy, who might have been a year and a half old, stood in front of the man's head, and had evidently been tumbling his hair. One hand held the father's neckerchief, and the little fellow was tugging at it as if it had been a halter, shouting with delight in his merry child's voice:

" Gee up, donkey! Gee up!"—" *Captain Veneno.*"

The Account-Book

OLD Gaffer Buscabeatas was already beginning to stoop at the time when the events occurred which I am going to relate; for he was now sixty years of age, and of these sixty years he had spent forty cultivating a garden bordering on the shore of La Costilla.

In the year in question he had cultivated in this garden some wonderful pumpkins, as large as the ornamental globes on the breastwork of some massive bridge, that at the time of our story were beginning to turn yellow, inside and out, which is the same as saying that it was the middle of June. Old Buscabeatas knew by heart the particular form and the stage of maturity at which it had arrived of every one of these pumpkins, to each of which he had given a name, and especially of the forty largest and finest specimens, which were already crying out, "Cook me!" and he spent the days contemplating them affectionately, and saying in melancholy accents, "Soon we shall have to part!"

At last, one evening, he made up his mind to the sacrifice, and marking out the best fruits of those beloved vines which had cost him so many anxieties, he pronounced the dreadful sentence. "To-morrow," he said, "I shall cut from their stalks these forty pumpkins and take them to the market at Cadiz. Happy the man who shall eat of them!"

And he returned to his home with slow step, and spent the night in such anguish as a father may be supposed to feel on the eve of his daughter's wedding-day.

"What a pity to have to part from my dear pumpkins!" he would sigh from time to time in his restless vigil. But presently he would reason with himself, and end his reflections by saying, "And what else can I do but sell them? That is what I have raised them for. The least they will bring me is fifteen pesos!"

Judge, then, what was his consternation, what his rage and despair, on going into the garden on the following morning, to find that during the night he had been robbed of his forty pumpkins! Not to weary the reader, I will only say that his emotion, like that of Shakespeare's Jew, so admirably represented, it is said, by the actor Kemble, reached the sublimity of tragedy as he frantically cried:

"Oh, if I could only find the thief! If I could only find the thief!"

Poor old Buscabeatas presently began to reflect upon the matter with calmness, and comprehended that his beloved treasures could not be in Rota, where it would be impossible to expose them for sale without risk of their being recognized, and where, besides, vegetables bring a very low price.

"I know, as well as if I saw them, that they are in Cadiz!" he ended. "The scoundrel! the villain! the thief must have stolen them between nine and ten o'clock last night, and got off with them at midnight on the freight-boat. I shall go to Cadiz this morning on the hour-boat, and it will surprise me greatly if I do not catch the thief there, and recover the children of my toil."

After he had thus spoken, he remained for some twenty minutes longer on the scene of the catastrophe, whether to caress the mutilated vines, to calculate the number of pumpkins that were missing, or to formulate a declaration of the loss sustained, for a possible suit; then, at about eight o'clock, he bent his steps in the direction of the wharf.

The hour-boat was just going to sail. This was a modest coaster which leaves Cadiz every morning at nine o'clock precisely, carrying passengers, as the freight-boat leaves Cadiz every night at twelve, laden with fruits and vegetables.

The former is called the hour-boat because in that space of time, and occasionally even in forty minutes, if the wind is favorable, it makes the three leagues which separate the ancient village of the Duke of Arcos from the ancient city of Hercules.

It was, then, half past ten in the morning on the before-mentioned day when old Buscabeatas passed before a vegetable-stand in the market of Cadiz, and said to the bored policeman who was accompanying him:

"Those are my squashes! Arrest that man!" and he pointed to the vender.

"Arrest me!" cried the vender, astonished and enraged. "These squashes are mine; I bought them!"

"You will have to prove that before the judge!" answered old Buscabeatas.

"I say no!"

"I say yes!"

"Thief!"

"Vagabond!"

"Speak more civilly, you ill-mannered fellows! Decent men ought not to treat one another in that way!" said the policeman tranquilly, giving a blow with his closed fist to each of the disputants.

By this time a crowd had gathered, and there soon arrived also on the scene the inspector of public markets.

The policeman resigned his jurisdiction in the case to his Honor, and when this worthy official had learned all the circumstances relating to the affair, he said to the vender majestically:

"From whom did you purchase those squashes?"

"From Fulano, a native of Rota," answered the person thus interrogated.

"It could be no one else!" cried old Buscabeatas. "He is just the one to do it! When his own garden, which is a very poor one, produces little, he takes to robbing the gardens of his neighbors!"

"But, admitting the supposition that forty pumpkins were stolen from you last night," said the inspector, turning to the old gardener and proceeding with his examination, "how do you know that these are precisely your pumpkins?"

"How?" replied old Buscabeatas. "Because I know

them as well as you know your daughters, if you have any! Don't you see that they have grown up under my care? Look here: this one is called Roly-Poly, this one Fat-Cheeks, this one Big-Belly, this one Ruddy-Face, this Manuela, because it reminded me of my youngest daughter."

And the poor old man began to cry bitterly.

"That may be all very well," replied the inspector; "but it is not enough for the law that you should recognize your pumpkins. It is necessary also that the authorities be convinced of the preexistence of the article in dispute, and that you identify it with incontrovertible proofs. Gentlemen, there is no occasion for you to smile. I know the law!"

"You shall see, then, that I will very soon prove to the satisfaction of everybody present, without stirring from this spot, that these pumpkins have grown in my garden!" said old Buscabeatas, to the no little surprise of the spectators of this scene. And laying down on the ground a bundle which he had been carrying in his hand, he bent his knees until he sat upon his heels, and quietly began to untie the knotted corners of the handkerchief.

The curiosity of the inspector, the vender, and the chorus was now at its height.

"What is he going to take out of that handkerchief?" they said to themselves.

At this moment a new spectator joined the crowd, curious to see what was going on, whom the vender had no sooner perceived than he exclaimed:

"I am very glad that you have come, Fulano! This man declares that the squashes which you sold me last night, and which are now here present, listening to what we are saying about them, were stolen. Answer, you!"

The newcomer turned as yellow as wax, and made a movement as if to escape, but the bystanders detained him by force, and the inspector himself ordered him to remain. As for old Buscabeatas, he had already confronted the supposed thief, saying to him:

"Now you are going to see something good."

Fulano, recovering his self-possession, answered:

"It is you who ought to see what you are talking about, for if you do not prove, as prove you cannot, your accusation, I shall have you put in prison for libel. These pumpkins were mine. I cultivated them, like all the others that I brought this year to Cadiz, in my garden, and no one can prove the contrary!"

"Now you shall see!" repeated old Buscabeatas, loosening the knots of the handkerchief and spreading out its contents on the ground.

And there were scattered over the floor a number of fragments of pumpkin stalks, still fresh and dripping sap, while the old gardener, seated on his heels and unable to control his laughter, addressed the following discourse to the inspector and the wondering bystanders:

"Gentlemen, have any of you ever paid taxes? If you have, you must have seen the big green book of the collector, from which he tears off your receipt, leaving the stub or end, so as to be able to prove afterward whether the receipt is genuine or not."

"The book you mean is called the account-book," said the inspector gravely.

"Well, that is what I have here, the account-book of my garden—that is to say, the stalks to which these pumpkins were attached before they were stolen from me. And in proof of what I say, look here! This stalk belongs to this pumpkin; no one can doubt it. This other—you can see for yourselves—belonged to this other. This is thicker—it must belong to this one. This to that one. This to that other."

And as he spoke he went fitting a stub or peduncle to the hole which had been made in each pumpkin as it was pulled from the stalk, and the spectators saw with surprise that the irregular and capricious-shaped ends of the peduncles corresponded exactly with the whitish circles and the slight hollows presented by what we might call the cicatrices of the pumpkins.

Every one present, including the policeman, and even the inspector himself, then got down on their heels and began to help old Buscabeatas in his singular accountant's work, crying out with childlike delight:

"He is right! He is right! There is not a doubt of it! Look! This belongs to this one. This to that one. That one there belongs to this. This belongs to that!" And the bursts of laughter of the grown people were mingled with the whistling of the boys, the abuse of the women, the tears of joy and triumph of the old gardener, and the shoves that the policeman gave to the convicted thief, as if they were all impatient to see him off to prison.

Needless to say that the policeman had that pleasure. Fulano was immediately compelled to restore to the vender the fifteen pesos he had received from him, the vender handed these over at once to old Buscabeatas, and the latter departed for Rota, highly delighted, although he kept repeating all the way home:

"How handsome they looked in the market! I should have brought Manuela back with me to eat for supper to-night, and save the seeds."—"*Moors and Christians,*" *Tales collected and published by The Cassell Company.*

Leopoldo Alas

Doctor Pertinax

SAINT PETER was polishing the large knocker of the gate of heaven, leaving it as bright as the sun—which is not to be wondered at, since the knocker Saint Peter was cleaning *is* the sun we see appearing every morning in the east.

The holy porter, merrier than his colleagues at Madrid, was humming some little air not unlike *Ca ira* of the French.

"Hullo! You get up very early," said he, bending his head and staring at a person who had stopped before the threshold of the gate.

The unknown did not reply, but bit his lips, which were thin, pale, and dry.

"No doubt," continued Saint Peter, "you are the philosopher who was dying last night? What a night you made me pass, friend! I never closed my eyes once, thinking you might be likely to knock. My last orders were not to let you wait a moment, a piece of respect paid to your sort here in heaven. Well, welcome, and come in. I can't leave the gate. Go through, and then straight on."

The stranger did not stir from the threshold, but fixed his little blue eyes on the venerable bald head of Saint Peter, who had turned his back to go on rubbing up the sun.

The newcomer was thin, short, and sallow, with somewhat feminine movements, neat in his attire, and without a hair on his face. He wore his shroud elegantly and nicely adjusted, and he measured his gestures with academic severity.

After gazing for some time at Saint Peter working, he wheeled round, and was about to return on the journey he had come he knew not how; but he found he was standing above a gloomy abyss, in which the darkness almost seemed palpable, and a furious tempest was roaring, with flashes of livid light at intervals like lightning. There was not a trace of any stairs, and the machine by which he dimly remembered he had mounted was not in sight either.

" Sir," exclaimed he, in a vibrating and acrid voice, " may I know what this means? Where am I? Why was I brought here? "

" Ah, you haven't gone yet! I am very glad, for I had forgotten something." And pulling his memorandum-book out of his pocket, the saint moistened the point of the pencil between his lips and asked:

" Your name? "

" I am Dr. Pertinax, author of the book stereotyped in its twentieth edition, called *Philosophia Ultima.*"

Saint Peter was not a quick writer, and of all this had only put down " Pertinax."

" Well, Pertinax of what? "

" Of what? Oh, I see—you mean from where? just as they say Thales of Miletus or Parmenides of Elea."

" Exactly, Quixote of la Mancha."

" Write down Pertinax of Torrelodones. And now, may I know what this farce means? "

" This farce? "

" Yes, sir. I am the victim of a farce. This is a comedy. My enemies, my colleagues, with the help of subtle artifices and theatrical machinery, exalting my mind with some beverage, have doubtless prepared all this. But the deception is useless. My power of reasoning is above all these appearances, and protests with a mighty voice against this low trickery. Neither masks nor lime-lights are of any avail, for I am not taken in by such palpable effrontery, and I say what I always said, and which is enframed on page 315 of my *Philosophia Ultima,* note *b* of the subnote Alpha, *i.e.,* that after death the deception of appearances will not exist, and there will no longer be any desire for life, *nolite vivere*, which is only a chain of shadows linked with desires, etc. Therefore, either I have died, or I have not died. If I have died, it cannot possibly be I as I was when alive half an hour ago, and all that I see around me, as it can only be a representation, is not, for I am not. But if I have not died, and am myself, what I was and am, it is clear that although what I see around me exists in me by representation, it is not what my enemies wish me to believe, but an unworthy farce designed to frighten me. But 'tis in vain, for——"

And the philosopher swore like a coal-heaver; and the swearing was not the worst, for he lifted up his voice toward heaven, the inhabitants of which were beginning to awake at the noise, while some of the blest were already descending by the staircase of clouds, tinged some as.with woad, others with a sea-blue.

Meanwhile Saint Peter held his sides with both hands to keep from bursting into the laughter with which he was nearly choking. Pertinax became more irritated at the saint's laughter, and the latter had to stop to try and pacify him by the following words:

" My dear sir, farces are of no avail here, nor is it a

question of deceiving you, but of getting you to heaven, which it appears you have merited for some good works of which I am ignorant. In any case, be easy and go up, for the inhabitants above are already astir, and you will find somebody who will conduct you to where all will be explained to your taste, so that not a shadow of doubt will remain, for doubts all disappear in this region, where the dullest thing is the sun which I am polishing."

"I do not say *you* are deceiving me, for you seem an honest man. The tricksters are others, and you only an instrument, unconscious of what you are doing."

"I am Saint Peter."

"They have persuaded you that you are; but there's no proof that you are."

"My dear sir, I have been porter here for more than eighteen hundred years."

"Apprehension, preconception——"

"Preconception fiddlesticks!" cried the saint, now somewhat angry. "I am Saint Peter, and you a philosopher, and, like all that come to us, you are an ignorant fool, with more than one bee in your bonnet!"

The gateway was now crowded with angels and cherubim, saints, male and female, and a number of the blest, who all formed a circle round the stranger and smilingly surveyed him.

From among them there stepped forth Saint Job. "I think," said he, "that this gentleman would be convinced that he had lived in error if he could see the universe as it actually is. Why not appoint a commission from among us to accompany Dr. Pertinax and show him the construction of the immense piece of architecture, as Lope de Vega says, whom I am sorry not to see among us."

Leopoldo Alas

Great was the respect for Saint Job, and they immediately proceeded to a nominal vote, which took up a good deal of time, as more than half the martyrology had repaired to the gate. The following were by the results appointed members of the commission: Saint Job, by acclamation; Diogenes, by a majority; and Saint Thomas the Apostle, by a majority. Saint Thomas of Aquinas and Duns Scotus had votes.

Dr. Pertinax gave way to the supplications of the commission, and consented to survey all the machinery and magic, with which they might deceive his eyes, said he, but not his mind.

"My dear fellow, don't be downhearted," said Saint Thomas, as he sewed some wings on to the doctor's shoulder-blades. "Look at me; I was an unbeliever, and——"

"Sir," replied Pertinax, "you lived in very different times, the world was then in its theological age, as Comte said, and I have passed through all those ages and have lived side by side with the *Criticism of Pure Reason* and the *Philosophia Ultima;* so that I believe in nothing, not even in the mother who bore me. I only believe in this, inasmuch as I know that I am, I am conscious, but without falling into the preconception of confounding representation with essence, which is unattainable, that is to say, excepting the being conscious, putting aside all that is not myself—and all being in myself—I *know,* by knowing that everything is represented—and I as everything else—by simply appearing to be what it is, and the reality of which is only investigated by another volitive and effective representation, a harmful representation, being irrational and the original sin of the Fall. Therefore, this apparent desire undone, nothing remains to explore, since not even the will for knowledge remains."

Only Saint Job heard the last word of this discourse, and, scratching his bald crown with his potsherd, he replied:

"The truth is, you philosophers are the very devil for talking nonsense; and don't be offended, but those things, whether in your head or imagination, as you please, will give you warm work to see them in reality as they are."

"Forward! Forward!" shouted Diogenes at this moment. "The sophists denied me motion, and you know how I proved it. Forward!"

And they began their flight through boundless space. Boundless? Pertinax thought it so, and said:

"Do you expect to show me all the universe?"

"Certainly," replied Saint Thomas.

"But since the universe—seemingly, of course—is infinite, how can you conceive the limit of space?"

"Conceive it, with difficulty; but see it, easily. Aristotle sees it every day, for he takes the most terrible walks with his disciples, and certainly he complained that the space for walking ended before the disputes of his peripatetics."

"But how can space have an end? If there is a limit, it will have to be nothing; but as nothing does not exist, it cannot form a boundary. For a boundary is something, and something apart from what is bounded."

Saint Job, who was already growing impatient, cut him short:

"Enough—enough talk! But you had better bend your head so as not to knock it, for we have arrived at that limit of space which cannot be conceived, and if you take a step more, you will break your head against that nothing you are denying."

And actually Pertinax saw there was nothing more beyond, wished to feel it, and bumped his head.

"But this can't be!" he exclaimed, while Saint Thomas applied to the bump one of those pieces of money which pagans take with them on their journey to the other world.

There was no help for it, they had to turn back, the universe had come to an end. But, ended or not, how beautiful shone the firmament with its millions and millions of stars!

"What is that dazzling light shining above there, higher than all the constellations? Is it some nebula unknown to the astronomers of the earth?"

"A pretty nebula!" replied Saint Thomas. "That is the Heavenly Jerusalem, from which we have just descended, and what is shining so are the diamond walls round the city of God."

"So that those marvels related by Chateaubriand, and which I thought unworthy of a serious man——"

"Are perfectly true, my friend. And now let us go and rest on that star passing below there, for i' faith, I am tired of so much going backward and forward."

"Gentlemen, I am not presentable," said Pertinax; "I have not yet doffed my shroud, and the inhabitants of this star will laugh at such indecorous garb."

The three guides of heaven all burst out laughing together. Diogenes was the first to exclaim:

"Though I should lend you my lantern, you would not meet a living soul in that star, nor in any other star."

"Of course," added Saint Job very seriously, "there are no inhabitants except on the earth. Don't talk such nonsense."

"This I cannot believe!"

"Well, let us go and show him," said Saint Thomas, who was already growing angry. And they journeyed from star to star, and in a few minutes had traversed all the Milky Way and the most distant starry systems. There was not a sign of life. They did not even encounter a flea on all the numerous globes they surveyed. Pertinax was horrified.

"This is the Creation!" he exclaimed. "What solitude! Come, show me the earth; I want to see that privileged region. By what I conjecture, all modern cosmography is a lie; the earth is still, and the center of all the celestial vault; and round her revolve the suns and planets, and she is the largest of all the spheres."

"Not at all," replied Saint Thomas; "astronomy is not mistaken; the earth revolves round the sun, and you will soon see how insignificant she appears. Let us see if we can find her among all that crowd of stars. *You* look for her, Saint Job; *you* have plenty of patience."

"I will!" exclaimed the saint of the potsherd, as he hooked his spectacles round his ears.

"It is like looking for a needle in a haystack. I see her! There she goes! Look! Look, how small! She looks like a microbe!"

Pertinax looked at the earth and sighed.

"And are there no inhabitants except on that mote?"

"Nowhere else."

"And the rest of the universe is empty?"

"Empty."

"Then of what use are such millions and millions of stars?"

"As lamps. They are the public illumination of the earth. And they are also useful for singing praises to the Almighty. And they serve as eke-outs in poetry, and you can't deny they are very pretty."

" But all empty ? "

" Every one ! "

Pertinax remained in the air for a good time, sad and thoughtful. The edifice of his *Philosophia Ultima* was threatening to collapse. Upon seeing that the universe was so different from what reason demanded, he began to believe in the universe. That brusk lesson of reality was the rude and cold contact with material which his spirit needed in order to believe. " It is all so badly arranged, but perhaps it is true ! " thus thought the philosopher. Suddenly he turned to his companions, and asked them, " Does hell exist ? "

The three sighed, made gestures of compassion, and replied, " Yes, it exists."

" And condemnation is eternal ? "

" Eternal."

" A great injustice ! "

" A terrible reality ! " replied the three in chorus.

Pertinax wiped his brow with his shroud. He was perspiring philosophy. He began to believe that he was in the other world. The injustice of everything convinced him. " Then the cosmogony and the theogony of my infancy was the truth ? "

" Yes, the first and only philosophy."

" Then I am not dreaming ? "

" No."

" A confessor—I want a confessor ! " groaned the philosopher; and he swooned into the arms of Diogenes.

When he awoke he found himself in his bed. His old servant and the priest were by his side.

' Here is the confessor, sir, for whom you asked."

Pertinax sat up, stretched out both hands, and, looking at the confessor with frightened eyes, cried out:

"I say and repeat, that all is simply a stage play, and that I am the victim of a wretched farce!"

And then he really expired.—"*Trumpet-Blasts.*"

Palacio Valdés

Founding a Provincial Newspaper

THE stage was almost full. More chairs were brought
from the actors' dressing-rooms, the most aristocratic resi-
dents of Sarrio took their seats, and then ensued a consultation to decide who was to be the chairman of the meeting. In
this there seemed to be some difficulty in coming to an agreement, and the public gave signs of impatience. The majority
was of opinion that the honor of sitting behind the pine-
wood table was due to Don Rosendo, but he declined it with
a modesty much redounding to his credit. At last, however,
he took the chair, as he saw the public was getting tired,
and the applause was tremendous. Fresh and wearisome
discussion ensued as to who was to open the meeting. Alvaro Peña, a man of impulse and action, finally took a few
steps toward the curtain, and said in a loud voice:
" Gentlemen."
" Sh! Sh! Silence!" cried several voices, and silence
reigned.
" Gentlemen, the object of this meeting is no other, eh?
than for us to unite in the support of the material and moral
interests of Sarrio. Some days ago our most worthy president informed me that they were deteriorating, eh? and that
it was necessary to support them at all costs. Gentlemen,
there are many questions at issue in Sarrio at this critical
time—the question of the covered market, the question of
the cemetery, the question of the road to Rodillero, the question of the slaughter-house, and many others; and I said to
my worthy friend, the only means of solving these problems

is to call a meeting at which all the Sarrienses can freely give their opinions."

"What?" cried a sharp voice from the gallery.

Peña darted an angry look in the direction of the sound, and, as he was known to be a violent man, and had a great, fierce mustache, the fellow trembled in his skin, and did not venture to make a second ejaculation.

"My good friend, whose large heart and love of progress is known to all, said to me some time ago that he was of the same opinion, and that, moreover, he had a plan that he was anxious to lay before this illustrious assembly. Therefore we have called our friends of Sarrio to a public meeting, and here we are—because we have come."

This collapse produced an excellent effect on the audience, who laughed good-naturedly.

"Gentlemen," continued the captain, encouraged by the sound of merriment, "I believe that what this place requires is to be roused from its state of lethargy to the life of reason and progress, eh? to rise to the height of the progress of the century, to take stock of itself and its powers. Hitherto Sarrio has been a town under the sway of theocracy; plenty of midday services, sermons, and rosaries, and no thought of the advance of its interests and the knowledge of anything useful. We must get out of this state, eh? we must shake off the theocratic yoke. A place governed by priests is always a backward and a squalid place." (*Laughter and applause, mingled with hisses.*)

The officer spoke better at the conclusion of his speech, and even acquired a certain self-assurance during his denunciation of priestcraft.

"May I be allowed to say a word?" cried a clear voice from a box.

" Who is it? Who is it?" asked the audience and the dignitaries of the stage of one another.

" It is Perinolo's son."

" Who?"

" Perinolo's son. Perinolo's son."

These words were repeated in a low tone all over the theater. . . .

" Who asked permission to speak?" queried Don Rosendo.

" Suarez—Sinforoso Suarez," said the youth who had asked for the floor, bending over the rail.

" Then you have it, Señor Suarez."

The young man coughed, ran the fingers of both hands through his hair, leaving it rougher and more tumbled than ever, put on his glasses that he wore hanging by a string, and said:

" Gentlemen."

The quiet, impressive tone with which he said this word, the long pause that followed it, during which he fixed his glasses on his nose and looked at the audience in a superior way, inspired silence and attention.

" After the brilliant speech which has just been given us by Señor Peña, my respected friend, the illustrious harbor-master of this port" (the captain, who had never spoken to Suarez more than three times in his life, bowed graciously), " the assembly is quite convinced of the generous and patriotic feelings which prompted the promoters of this meeting. There is nothing so beautiful, nothing so grand, nothing so sublime as to see a town met together to discuss the dearest, highest interests of life. Ah, gentlemen, when listening just now to Señor Peña I imagined myself in the Agora of Athens, a free citizen, with other citizens, free as myself, discussing the destiny of my country; I imagined I heard the ardent, eloquent words of one of those great orators who adorned the Hellenic State. Why, the eloquence of my dear friend, Señor Peña, was like the overwhelming passion that characterized Demosthenes, the prince of orators, and like the fluency and elegance that distinguished the discourses of Pericles. (*Pause, with his hand to his glasses.*) He was bright and animated, like Cleon; deliberate and temperate, like Aristides; his intonation was quiet and precise, like that of Esquines, and his voice was pleasant to the ear, like that of Isocrates. Ah, gentlemen, I, like the eloquent orator who has preceded me on the subject, desire that the place which gave me birth may awake to the life of progress, to the life of liberty and justice. Sarrio! What sweet recollections, what ineffable happiness does this single word awaken in my soul! Here were passed the days of my childhood. Here my mind began to form. Here love made my heart palpitate for the first time. Elsewhere my mind has been enriched by the knowledge of science, and the grand ideas engendered by the study of law; here my soul has been nourished by the sweet and holy feelings of the hearth. Elsewhere my intelligence has been sharpened by polemics and the light of ideas; here my affections have been fostered by tender family love. Gentlemen, I will say it again, come what may, Sarrio is called to a great destiny! It has a right to be one of the first towns on the Biscayan coast, an emporium of activity and riches, by reason of the excellent position which Nature has given it, as well as the integrity, industry, and the great gift of intelligence of its inhabitants."

(*"Bravo! Bravo!" Unanimous and loud applause.*)

The silence, caused more by surprise than any bad feeling, was now broken, and the "bravos" and applause continued without intermission. Never had the industrious, honest, intelligent people of Sarrio heard any one speak so fluently and eloquently before.

"That discourse was a revelation of the modern parliamentary style!" So Alvaro Peña said when the meeting was over.

The speech continued half an hour longer, amid the increasing enthusiasm of the audience, when one of the notabilities on the platform thought that his throat must be dry, and that it was time to give him a glass of sugared water. The idea was communicated in an undertone to the president, who interrupted the orator with the remark:

"If Señor Suarez is fatigued, he can rest. I am going to have a glass of water sent him."

These words were received with a murmur of approval.

"I am not tired, Señor President," the orator replied gently.

(*"Yes, yes; rest. Make him rest. Let him have a glass of water. He will hurt himself. Let him have a few drops of anise."*)

The audience, suddenly inspired with tender sympathy, manifested quite a maternal solicitude for Perinolo's son, who, inflated with delight, smiled on the audience and continued:

"Fatigue is fitting for valiant soldiers. Those who, like myself, are accustomed to the tribune (he had spoken a few times in the Academy of Jurisprudence in Lancia), do not easily become fatigued."

We must now say that Mechacar, a shoemaker, a neighbor, and a rival of many years' standing of Señor José Maria Perinolo, who had known Sinforoso from his birth, and had often given him two or three beatings with the strap, when on his return from school he annoyed him by calling him by some contemptuous nickname, was in the gallery with

his hands resting on the rail, and his face, alert and attentive, on his hands. No enthusiasm shone in those eyes under the lowering brows, as in those of the others; but
envy, hatred, and malice were visible on the countenance.
When the honeyed words of his rival fell upon his ears
he felt powerless to stand the farce, and he called out in a
rage:

" Stop that rubbish, you fool ! "

(*Indescribable indignation of the audience. All eyes were
turned to the gallery. Voices were heard saying:*)

" Who is this brawler? To prison with him! Out with
the fool ! "

The president asked with terrible severity:

" Are we in a civilized town, or among Hottentots ? "

The question thus formulated produced a profound impression upon the audience. Suarez, slightly pale, and in an
agitated voice, finally said:

" If the meeting desire it, I am ready to sit down."

(*"No, no! Go on!" Loud and prolonged applause for
the orator.*)

The indignation against the rude disturber increased to
such a degree that sounds of threats were audible, and several shook their fists in the direction whence the voice had
proceeded. Alvaro Peña, the Greek orator, more indignant
than anybody, finally went up to the gallery and put Mechacar out of the theater by force, amid the applause of the
public.

The storm abated, the orator continued. He made a wide
digression through the fields of history to prove that from
the Roman conquest, when Spain was divided into citerior
and ulterior Hispania, and afterward into Tarraco, Betica,
and Lusitania, and so on down to the present day, the Sar-

rienses had on all occasions given proof of a powerful intellect, very superior to that of the people of Nieva.

Such assertions were received with great signs of approval. Then suddenly passing into the region of law, he gently touched upon branches of knowledge that are not common, particularly in Sarrio—the science of Tribonianus and Papinianus.

On arriving at a certain point he said, with a modesty that did him credit:

"What I have just observed, señor, has no scientific value whatsoever. Every boy knows it who has made the acquaintance of the pandectas."

Don Jeronimo de la Fuente, a schoolmaster of the town who had studied the modern methods of pedagogics, and knew something of Froebel and Pestalozzi, a celebrated man who had written a primer on irregular verbs and kept a telescope at his window always turned toward the heavens, now rose from his seat and said:

"Corporal punishment has been stopped in the schools for some years."

"I did not say *palmetas* [blows]; I said *pan-dec-tas,*" returned Suarez, smiling with some vexation.

Don Jeronimo was angry at having made such a mistake.

The orator continued, and finally resumed his seat, saying, like the eloquent officer who had preceded him, that Sarrio must awake to the life of progress; that it must arise from the lethargy in which it lay, and that she must take part in the struggle of ideas, which are always fruitful; and that she must let the radiant sun of civilization rise on her horizon.

"If it be true, as I have heard, that, thanks to the patriotic and generous initiative of a most worthy citizen of this town, that the Fourth Estate of modern powers is about to

celebrate its advent here; if, in fact, Sarrio will be presented
with a periodical which will reflect her legitimate aspirations,
let it be the palladium for the exercise of her intelligence,
the promoter of her dearest interests, the advanced protector
of her tranquillity and peace, the organ, in short, by which
it may have communion with the spiritual world. Let us
congratulate ourselves with all our hearts, and let us also
congratulate the illustrious patrician whose efforts will bring
to us a ray of this luminous star of the nineteenth century
which is called the press."

(*"Bravo! Bravo!" All eyes are turned to the chairman.
The face of Don Rosendo beams with dignity and delight.*)

After the son of Perinolo came Don Jeronimo de la Fuente.
The illustrious professor of the instruction of youth was very
anxious to rise in the eyes of the public after his slip about
the pandectas. He commenced by saying that he shared the
opinions of the worthy orator (notice that he did not say
eloquent, or illustrious, but worthy, nothing more) who had
preceded him on the subject; that he, destined by his profession to light the torch of science in infantile brains, could
not do less than be a devoted partizan of all modern enlight-
enment, more especially of that of the press. In corrobora-
tion of this statement he begged to say that as soon as a
periodical in Sarrio was an established fact he would have
the pleasure of laying before his fellow citizens the solution
of a problem which until now was considered insoluble—that
of the trisection of the angle—to which he had devoted much
time and trouble, and which, fortunately, now was crowned
with success. He spoke, moreover, with great emphasis on
other matters—of physical geography and astronomy, clearly
and briefly explaining the earth's rotation and progression,
the composition of air, the formation of the clouds and dew,

the origin of the salt of the sea, of springs and rivers, the scientific cause of tides, and also something about the cause of volcanoes. Afterward, just by the way, he passed on to an explanation of the celestial mechanism, and particularly the law of universal attraction, discovered by Newton, by which planets move round the sun in elliptic orbits. Then he explained with great brilliancy the nature of an ellipsis. Finally, speaking of our satellite, the moon, he remarked that the time of its revolution round the earth was sensibly diminishing, which indicated the decrease of its orbit. This, according to the orator, would sooner or later result in the moon falling into the earth, when both would be shattered. Don Jeronimo then resumed his seat, leaving the audience quite crushed under the weight of this alarming prophecy.

The proceedings went on until lamps were lighted. Don Rufo, the town doctor, a tall, lean man, with a pointed beard and gold eye-glasses, then got up and declared explicitly in a few words that thought was only a physiological function of the brain, and the soul an attribute of matter, and that the greater or less degree of intelligence in animals depends on the cerebral lobules and the weight of the brain. The orator computed that its weight in a man was three pounds and a half. Then he gave the calculation of the phosphoric matter that it contains. Man's brain contains more phosphorus than animals', while theirs have more than birds'. In children the quantity of phosphorus increases considerably at the natal hour, and it continues to increase rapidly with the course of time. But in what part of the brain is the spark of intellectual activity situated? asked the orator. In his opinion this activity has its mainspring in the grayish or bluish substance, and in some way in the whitish substance, which is the conductor of such activity. He then spoke of the dura mater, the hemispheres of the brain, the frontal, parietal, and occipital parts of the skull, the function of the cerebrum, the seat of the cerebellum. Here the speaker conceived the happy idea of making a beautiful comparison between the circumlocutions of this gray substance and a heap of intestines thrown promiscuously together. All the faculties which we call the soul are nothing but functions of this gray substance, of this mass of intestines. The brain secretes thoughts, as the liver does bile. The orator concluded by saying that while humanity is ignorant of these truths it cannot rise from its present state of barbarism.

Navarro, the veterinary professor, who never wished to be behind the doctor, then asked leave to speak, and after a few words of congratulation on the inauguration of the " meeting " (all the speakers used the English term), he gave expression to a few very rational ideas on the gangrenous quinsy of the pig, and the treatment for its prevention. The orator hesitated, stuttered, and grew hot in the expression of his ideas, but this deficiency of language was compensated for by the novelty and interest of the subject, for numbers of these nice animals fell victims to quinsy at certain seasons in Sarrio.

In spite of the interest and respect with which the public listened to the discourse on the danger which threatened pig-farming, there were certainly signs of impatience to hear the president's speech. After the allusion of Perinolo's son to the fact of a journal, every one was anxious to have the news confirmed. While Navarro was talking a voice from the gallery cried:

" Let Don Rosendo speak ! "

And although this rude interruption was rebuked with a

prompt "Sh!" it was evident that they had had enough of Navarro.

At last the celebrated man of Sarrio, the standard-bearer of all progress, the illustrious patrician, Don Rosendo Belinchon's majestic figure rose behind the table.

(*"Silence! Sh! Sh! Silence, gentlemen! Attention! A little attention, please!"*)

These were the cries that proceeded from the crowd, although nobody dared move a finger, such was the anxiety to hear the president's remarks.

Like all men of a really superior mind and clear intelligence, Don Rosendo wrote better than he spoke. Nevertheless, his quiet mode of speech gave an impression of dignity that was wanting in the orators who had preceded him.

"Gentlemen (*pause*), I thank (*pause*) all the people (*pause*) who have assisted (*pause*) this afternoon (*pause*) at the meeting which I have had the honor to convene. (*Much longer pause, rife with expectation.*) I have a real pleasure (*pause*) in seeing gathered together in this place (*pause*) the most illustrious persons of the town (*pause*), and all those who, for one reason or another, are of consequence and importance."

(*"Bravo! Very good! Very good!"*)

After this exordium, received in such a flattering style, the orator maintained that he was moved by the desire to raise the intellectual tone of Sarrio. Then he added that the object of this meeting had only been that of raising this tone. (*Long applause.*) He considered himself too weak and incompetent to accomplish the task. (*"Yes, yes!" Applause.*) But he counted on—at least he thought he could count on—the support of the many men of feeling, patriotism, intelligence, and progress dwelling in Sarrio. (*Thunders of ap-*

plause.)   The means that he considered most efficacious to raise Sarrio to its rightful height, and to make it compete worthily with other towns, and even maritime towns of more importance, was the creation of an organ that would support its political, moral, and material interests.   " And, gentlemen (*pause*), although all the difficulties are not yet overcome (*pause*), I have the pleasure of informing this illustrious assembly " ("*Attention! Sh! Sh! Silence!*") " that perhaps in the ensuing month of August " ("*Bravo! Bravo!*" *Loud and frantic applause that interrupted the orator for some minutes*) " that perhaps in the ensuing month of August " ("*Bravo! Bravo! Silence!*") " the town of Sarrio will have a biweekly paper."—" *The Fourth Estate.*"